VOICES FROM THE ATTIC
VOLUME XVIII

Series Editor: Jan Beatty

THE CARLOW UNIVERSITY PRESS

ISBN 978-0-9847364-2-3

© 2012

Poetry Editor
Jan Beatty

Fiction Editor
Evelyn Pierce

Creative Nonfiction Editor
Nancy Kirkwood

Assistant Poetry Editors
Celeste Gainey
Liane Ellison Norman
Sarah Williams-Devereux

Copy Editor
Sarah Williams-Devereux

Editorial Assistance
Elise D'Haene

Second-Line Editor
Abbey Wamboldt

Thanks to:

Carlow University's division of University Communications
and External Relations;

Ellie Wymard, founder of the Madwomen;
Lou Boyle for continued mentorship;
Sigrid King for valued leadership;
Nancy Kirkwood, Evelyn Pierce, Ellen McGrath Smith,
    Stacey Waite, and Sarah Williams-Devereux for superb
    teaching and editing;
Elise D'Haene, Celeste Gainey, and Liane Ellison Norman
    for skilled editing;
Sarah Williams-Devereux for adept organization, planning,
    editing, and conjuring;
Abbey Wamboldt for assistance with editing;

The Madwomen for continued madness.

for Patricia Dobler

Contents

Introduction

Voices from the Attic Volume XVIII, is the best work from the Madwomen in the Attic Writing Workshops in poetry, fiction, and nonfiction at Carlow University, taught by myself, Nancy Kirkwood, Evelyn Pierce, Ellen McGrath Smith, Stacey Waite, and Sarah Williams-Devereux.

The Madwomen in the Attic are a group of women, ages 21-98, who meet weekly at Carlow to study the craft of writing. They are unique in their pursuits and in their method of workshop: as serious writers, they bring their poems, stories, and nonfiction drafts to class—but also, they bring a generous support for each other as they offer good feeling and solidarity as an integral part of the challenging and relentless work of writing.

The writers in this collection bring a range of aesthetic, ideals, concerns, and politics to the table. Their madness has been documented in their everyday revolutions of spirit: these are women who have experienced life's challenges on every level, and are still standing. On any given day when you enter a Madwomen class, you might find: a group of women in silence, reading; a group of women in an uproar of laughter; women engaged in spirited disagreement over a line in a poem; women eating pastries; a group of women talking about how to get published, the best strategies for submitting their work. You will always find: women engaged in head-down serious work on their writing; women sharing stories and strategies of living and survival.

The Madwomen are: lighting designers, screenwriters, middle-school teachers, psychiatrists, undergraduates, political activists, MFA students, massage therapists, attorneys, painters, photographers, college professors, and more. They are wild in their adventures and their dreams, and they are growing in numbers. This past year, the Madwomen classes have expanded to offer eight sections: five in poetry, two in fiction, and one in creative nonfiction. We expect this growth to continue to include more sections in creative nonfiction.

The Madwomen have gone wild this year with accomplishment, and, as always, we are proud to honor their success. Sheila Carter-Jones won the Naomi Long Madgett book award for poetry for her collection,

Three Birds Deep, published by Wayne State University Press. Shirley Snodey's chapbook of poems, *Barefoot on Southern Soil*, was published by MadBooks in 2012. Madwoman Lois Greenberg's full-length poetry collection, *Willing to Lie*, was also published by MadBooks this year. Angele Ellis's pantoum, "Josseline of the Desert," was a runner-up in the 2011 *Shine* journal poetry contest. Judith Brice's full-length collection of poems, *Renditions in a Palette*, will be published by Wordtech Communications in the Fall of 2013. Madwoman Marlene Goldsmith's poem, "Fashion's Cold Night," received an honorable mention in the Tupelo Press Spring 2011 Poetry Project contest. Dorit Brauer's creative nonfiction book, *Girls Don't Ride Motorbikes—A Spiritual Adventure Into Life's Labyrinth*, chronicles her 7,430 mile solo motorcycle adventure. In the world of e-books, Madwoman Alice Fuchs has published a new chapbook of poems, *god L*, and two novels, *Becoming Tourists and Virtual Gardener*. Madeleine Barnes was named a finalist for the Hungry Poets Prize, sponsored by the West Virginia University Department of English, and was accepted to the master's program at the National University of Ireland at Galway. Madwoman Emily Mohn was awarded a scholarship to Bennington College to pursue an MFA in creative writing (poetry). Congratulations to all! Other achievements of note include Madwoman Kayla Sargeson's graduation from Columbia College Chicago's MFA program, and her infamous return to Pittsburgh. Also, a big welcome to new Madwomen Celeste Gainey and Elise D'Haene, who have moved to Pittsburgh from Long Island.

We thank the Madwomen instructors, Nancy Kirkwood, Evelyn Pierce, Ellen McGrath Smith, Stacey Waite, and Sarah Williams-Devereux for their vital creativity and engaged teaching. We are thrilled to welcome two new instructors, poets Joy Katz and Nancy Krygowski, for the Spring, 2012 semester. Through each new incarnation, the Madwomen in the Attic grow daily in small and large revolutions: the brave writing and living of these amazing women. I am lucky to be a part of their wild, relentless imaginings and their terrific work.

—Jan Beatty
April, 2012

Fortification

In the car, in the cemetery for the famous,
I have found a good place to wail—
people will think I'm another mourner.
Brown seed-balls hang by the hair
from the sycamores. Late afternoon light
should be swallowed by now, but there's
a glow from someplace, probably the snow itself—
let it be gone. And it's far too late
for that lineman to see what he's doing,
shinnying up a tree with his ropes and electric saw.
But those branches have to go.
Let me be practical and clear:
I am not this sycamore, nor is it a figure for me.
Someone I love is not dead but gone.
When the lineman lops off the offending arms,
I can see the tree's pale under-skin below
its greenish bark. Not a dark tree. An embattled one.

PATRICIA DOBLER

VOICES FROM THE ATTIC
VOLUME XVIII

Cutting Limes on the Afternoon Joey Died

one lime
then two halves
then four pieces
then six chunks
I rock the handle hard
making sure the cut is clean

Stacie says:
Drink this. (Tequila)
Cut these. (More limes)
Focus on them.
one lime
then two halves
then four pieces
let it be five years from this
just five years, or even four,
let it be anything more than now
please let this be quick

two halves
four pieces
six chunks
thirty seconds
ten years

LISA ALEXANDER

The First Time I Saw Two Girls Kiss

We got away
with watching Cinemax at 3 AM in 1989
because Jenny Olini's mom slept
through giggling, crunching handfuls
of Fruity Pebbles from the box.
We wanted to see naked people on TV.

[Big blue pool cupped by palm
trees somewhere hot, like LA—
Skinny girls in pink bikinis, stilettos—
Put some lotion on my back
A brunette with a perm, a blonde with big
bangs, lay out on towels bitching
about their meatball muscle men—
Here, let me undo my straps
Hawaiian Tropic glistens on oily hands
You do me, and I'll do you
Simultaneously they rub each other's
shoulders, arms, neck, collarbone

down over white tan lines,
pinched nipples. Neither back off.
They tilt closer, kiss stiff kisses,
pointy tongues meet outside thin girl lips]

My stomach hurt. Jenny kept watching.
I had to say something, address this,
*I can't imagine ever   I don't care if
I never, ever could.*
Call it out, put some words on it.

The Birds

At the delimiter of a vicious winter
birds reappear on the twisted three-strand
Verizon umbilical cable
linking me to the rest of the world

A brilliant cardinal couple—regal
still, magisterial—sways gently
for a spell, nods
what-cheer, what-cheer
and by mutual assent soars side by side away

Flurries of sparrows—tan and grey
roll randomly on and off each other
like furry magnetized tennis balls
chip-chip-ssip, chip-chip-ssip, chip-ssip
and dart off one by one

The fossil record tells us
the birds have been doing this for millions
and millions of years

What will the digital record show?

The Doomed

Vissi d'arte, vissi d'amore

The trees around here are disappearing
About ten years ago the sycamores went
Experts give the ashes another ten
the oaks maybe twenty

The magnolia shading my front porch—
bark stripping, branches splitting—
remains only because I cannot let it go
I will not turn it in to the tree police!

Arched like longbows, suckers—*Sure sign of a tree
in trouble*—say the arborists
shoot up from the roots and briefly every spring
produce a wild, colossal, glorious ball of blossom—

ephemeral—like Tosca. Like Tosca
persistent, irresistible, unyielding
in her faith in the power of life and beauty
singing her heart out on the parapet.

Breaststroke

I.

Watching the blue
of Martha's eyes become
      the Caribbean,
deep and clear—
I forget I am in a hospice room,
      forget it's forty floors up,
      looking down
            into a wide calm bay,
the blue inviting me in again
      to follow her stride,
      Race me to the buoy and back!

II.

It's not easy to imagine
the world rotating
on an axis, and spinning
as you stand beside her, still,

restless, sleeping angel,
sand so hot it burns skin,
the woman only wanting
      to swim out—
shed confinement.

LAURIE ARNOLD

III.

The last thing you witness,
(as the mouth gasps
for a pocket of
          ocean sprayed air,
and mangos cut
dripping onto
fingers of memory,
teasing the fleshy fruit)

is a gesture of arms
moving through water,
the strong pull, the hearty kick,
and the rising for air.

IV.

How does *she* remember
this moment without water—
only blue eyes
chasing the tide out,
turquoise and dazzling?

Orange Popsicles and Pink Geraniums

Past the mulberry tree at the center of the cemetery, I got a good look at the white splotch on top of Grandma's headstone. It was a pair of gloves. Closer, I realized there was something else there, too. I quickened my pace until I could make out an unwrapped double orange Popsicle stuck to the gloves. A sticky trail ran across long empty fingers and down the front of her stone. Most families left flowers or crosses, didn't they? What was wrong with mine?

It was Marti, I would bet on it, Grandma's adopted half-sister, whatever that was. Grandma collected family members. I have more relatives than a character in a Dostoyevsky novel. Some of them I could do without, including Marti. Still, after five years, I was pretty sure that Marti was the only one besides me who would visit Grandma on her birthday.

In the old days, wherever Grandma was, sooner or later, Marti would show up. I was never sure if Marti liked me at all. Once she asked if I ever left the house without mascara. Grandma laughed and hugged me and said, "Of course she doesn't." She gave Marti that little half-wink that I thought was ours alone. They were always putting their heads together over something—that was Grandma's term for cooking up mischief.

"Brought you a flower," I said, addressing the sticky headstone. "Hope you like it." I was glad no one was around to hear the petulance in my voice. Grandma liked white gloves and Popsicles, especially orange ones. As far as I knew, she'd never said anything about geraniums. I stood to the side of the stone, careful not to step on Grandma, my potted geranium in one hand, garden spade in the other.

I watched the Popsicle for a while in its undisturbed melt. It spread itself wide and flat across the gloves. A thin trickle laced and pooled over the etched letters of Cecelia Margaret Dunlap. I focused on the Margaret, my name.

I wanted to hate the whole sticky mess, but in the May sunshine, it was beautiful—a Dali-esque still life of the passing of summers, the passing of my Grandma with her big smile and oranged and sweetened Popsicle lips. My lost Grandma who wore white kid gloves to weekly mahjong parties. A steady melt of orange soaked the glove's index finger. I remembered that Grandma had often said that Marti was an artist.

In a moment of bravery, I plopped myself down on the ground right in front of the stone, like I was sitting on Grandma's lap. Maybe I didn't have to be so perfect all the time. I dug into the dirt with the little spade I'd brought and set the geranium with five pink flowers into the hole directly under the drip from the glove's index finger.

While I was patting the dirt back around the stem, I heard footsteps. I looked up and there was Marti sucking on a single banana Pop, standing right on top of Grandma, looking down at me. I was about to tell her to get off of Grandma, didn't she know better than to be stepping on a grave? Her perfect offering stung me even more when I saw her open face, those eager eyes.

"That's wonderful, Margaret," she said, before I could light into her.

"What?"

"The fuchsia. Most people would have picked red. And where you planted it, too. Look, you and me get to watch the orange Popsicle melt right into it. Reminds me exactly of Cecelia's apron, that orange and pink one she wore every Sunday when she baked. It's like your Grandma sent us both out to make her a masterpiece today." She narrowed her eyes and they looked a little less eager, like maybe she knew what I'd been thinking about her.

I couldn't bring myself to answer and looked down. When I looked back up, her face was as open as ever. Maybe she didn't know after all. Maybe I was saved. In my heart, I thanked Grandma for slowing my tongue, for rescuing me from casting an ugly blight on our birthday offering. I bit my lip to make sure no words flew out before I had a chance to mull them over.

After a minute, I patted the space next to me, the other half of Grandma's lap. "Want to sit here and watch the melt together?" I asked.

Marti let herself plop to the ground with a groan and a laugh. The slack skin under her arm jiggled. Her row of mismatched bracelets clinked. "My knees aren't what they used to be," she said.

I reached out to steady her. "Want a taste?" she asked and stuck the banana Pop near my nose while she worked to tuck her legs under her tent of a dress.

"Nope," I said.

We didn't talk anymore, just sat there while Grandma's orange Popsicle went to mush and leaked all over the place, dripping down the front of Cecelia Margaret Dunlap onto the pink geranium petals in a slow river of remembrance. When the gloves were stiff and the double sticks were bare, I rose to my feet. I pulled Marti to standing with both my hands. Her fingers were bent, the backs of her hands spotted, but her grip was strong and warm. She let go and brushed dirt and grass clippings from the back of her muumuu. We stood in silence. A dog barked and the hum of a lawnmower started up somewhere in the distance. We faced each other. Her eyes were moist and not so much eager now as knowing—full of a sad patience and a weird detached love, like the statues that ringed the altar at St. Stanislaus where we'd both bade our final farewells to Grandma.

"That was excellent," I said, finally.

Marti nodded and squeezed my hand. "We really put our heads together on that one."

EILEEN ARTHURS

Don't You

A note is off, but I can't tell which, and I've fucked up,
but we're on the same page. *Do you love me?*
you don't remember asking. Yes I do, your shirts
smell good, and I like when you talk about biology,
saying the body does this, does that—show me. You slip
your note cards into my dress, they fall out one by one
we're dancing and then we're walking to the diner
and you have quarters for a song,
you choose the longest one of all, the worst,
maybe I've learned all I need to know
and our friends black out on the apartment floor,
we draw constellations between their shoes,
their party clothes, we scratch their elbows
with a fine-tip pen, and no one knows the name
of the person sleeping in the corner, he's holding
my pillow and looking at peace with some greater part
of the universe, *that kid's gone*, you say,
and he is, he is. You'll stay tonight until forever,
you'll be here at the end of my life, won't you?
I'll untangle my body from yours, face
the daylight spread across the wall. I will.
It's happening now and happens all the time,
and I'll be awake before you and our friends
making sure all of them are breathing, collecting
pieces of myself from them, from you.

I did not abandon the right things.

A plane wing ascends,
one smooth angle
cutting off the earth

and only what's below
is clear to me, above
seems much more limitless.

A woman asks to hold my hand,
reminds me of my sister in an x-ray gown,
I pulled the metal over her
she was too frail to stay upright
flash: her bones in crooked blue

what if every time
I take the heaviest things
and make them light
they are subtracted
somewhere else?

I carry our separation well
but distances add up,
the difference hardly visible

but every now and then I see her
as she was:
sick and small, she only knew
what I described

I didn't speak to anyone
but her, I thought
to say a word to someone else
would take away
from what it meant

　　　　　　　　　　　　MADELEINE BARNES

so I told her simple things,
the images I waited for
occurred to me because I thought
they wouldn't stay with her for long

in this light her weightlessness
appears to me in bolder forms
a window placed above the earth
that gives her shape
and cuts me off from her.

At Swallow Falls

Great white pines
and tall hemlocks
hover silently—

iced evergreen
thought to be three
hundred years old

at least, the oldest
hemlock and white
pine in all the country—

virgin queens, regally
green in this snowy
forest never logged

by man, their majesty,
their eerie ancientness,
is blanketed by the

snow that extends
itself across centuries
as together we make

our way along trails
iced under white, green
ferns magically still

green at our feet in
February, together with
you at Swallow Falls.

The Walking Dead

At the Hippodrome
for eleven cents
on Saturdays, she
watched the zombies—
crowded into the second floor balcony
pounded her feet
to Boris Karloff's resurrection
from the dead
stomped cheerfully
arms straight out in front raised
nineteen thirty-eight
seven-years-old poor
but for eleven cents
all day all the way
home to the Veteran's Housing Project
she pounded her feet
arms raised every Saturday,
my mother, the zombie of Liverpool Street

Begonias

Her husband hated the begonias
especially when the sun would burn
what he called their 'ugly apron' petals.

Something made him queasy.
He called them Old-Lady Flowers.

> She said:
> *I love their bright-throats,*
> *pale and thin as baby eyelids,*
> *the bronze-green leaves, deep-veined*
> *as river valleys.*
>
> *They never 'forget themselves'*
> *or aspire to rose or orchid—*

But her fulsome praise
just drifted in the wind.

> *Will I stand alone,*
> *staring hard at gutted soil?*
>
> *Will I see nothing*
> *but a drip-drop rain?*

One day with shovels, spades and gloves,
they tore into the soil, tugging at the roots

until whether extravagant as gold
or dull as muddy bells,

every border flower was gone.

JOAN E. BAUER

I Wake Up at 5 AM & Think I'm Hans Castorp

Only I'm on this canyon & can see goats grazing,
eucalyptus etched against the morning sky.
My whole life, a *bildungsroman*.

Half-asleep, I start reading my old college lecture notes
from when my lanky young professor was moonlighting
helping Jim Morrison with his poetry before Morrison
was famous, before he was everywhere, before he OD'd
in the back room of a Paris bar.

Years ago, my friend Sharon and I were in Paris
& while she was at the Château de Malmaison,
I stood in the rain near Morrison's grave
as bedraggled kids brought red and yellow roses.

Two cups of coffee, the orange dawn spreading.
Sharon is moving back to Pittsburgh. I'm moving
to Venice, California. But she says she'll visit me,
as she loves the canals.

In the first day's lecture, my young professor said:
People you meet in literature are not who you'll meet in life.
I don't know what that means.

Aging Time

Age is a state of mind, hair, skin and joints,

better with rolled joints or now a well-earned

Grand Marnier on the rocks with

light sparking big stones on crooked fingers

and good talk glowing the room to rainbow.

In the morning, life springs and flows swifter

with the Bible and Prophetess Anna

(Luke 2:36) who had to be over a hundred

saw her Messiah maybe cradled Him in her

wrinkled frail arms knew too that nano-

second Being yes to whatever remains.

JOAN HUBER BERARDINELLI

Have to Do

Put marked-up Best Buy flyer
on *Writer's Chronicle* stack with
the 2008 *Utne Reader*, try not to hear
Mother's "You <u>never</u> put things back"
from fifty years ago, find Madwomen
file in shopping bag from Cuba, let
the dogs out, pay the Duquesne Light
bill, pay his parking ticket, find my checkbook,
Where the hell's my coffee cup?
silence Mother's daily "place for
everything and everything in its place,"
change the dogs' water, buy Chardonnay,
find a pen, sort yesterday's mail, pile
his on *Trade-a-Planes*, add green beans
to Sandi's kibble, spoon out Alpo
for old Chui, find my shopping list, write
a note for the cleaning lady, find the
coffee beans, remember to buy more
Colombian, let the dogs back in,
sort out pens that don't work, ask
Mother to get out of my head, dig out
coffee filters, feed the dogs, find my
to-do list, count out vitamins,
find instructions on humor writing.

Absence

It wasn't just her voice, glued to my tongue,

but her insistence to keep on living. She died

when I was seven. Vanished. Leaving behind

the perfect symmetry of her death and my life.

Her absence was the square root of my childhood.

The stone that wasn't there became the question

I couldn't ask, so I stopped wishing and learned

how to make decisions. These are her remains:

a moth-eaten sweater, some paper dolls, journals,

her wedding ring, and a postcard from Paris

she sent me when I was 3 years old. Fifty years

later she insists on placing her wide fresh mouth

over mine—and blowing the air out of my lungs.

How shall I organize my grief? If I put her in a box

I could lift the lid, and inhale the scent of mohair.

The paper dolls we played with could be laid to rest.

Or I could scoop out a grave with a rounded spoon.

But I think I'll have a picnic with her ashes,

spreading flesh and petals in the bleak half-light

with milky breath.

KAREN KORNBLUM BERNTSEN

Yom Kippur

On this day of atonement I fall asleep in a hotel

in a darkened room

on the eighteenth floor.

My dreams are seams—strong as rope—

with thick stitches

they fasten my days.

A space in the drapes defines a slice

of who shall live

and who shall die.

But I am spread on the bed like a compass rose,

dreaming in all directions.

A prayer decomposing in my mouth,

a knife of sunlight across my face.

Dressmaking With My Mother

A box of old patterns: Butterick, Simplicity, Vogue,
hand-made ones cut from daily newspapers,
brings back memories of you, replicating dresses

displayed on mannequins in the windows
of Gimbels, Kaufmann's and Horne's.
You used newsprint to precisely cut patterns

with your professional-grade Wiss scissors
you always kept in the original blue box.
We flipped through page after page of fashions

in Couturier sections of Vogue Patterns until we found
the right one for the occasion: Confirmation, 1948.
White pique suit, flared skirt, gold buttons.

Grade School Graduation, 1950. Blue cotton dress,
satin ribbon woven through white lace bodice.
Wedding, 1964. Bone crepe gown, square neck,

train, empire waist. No ornamentation.
We pushed bolt after bolt of fabric aside until we saw
the right one, purchased matching thread, zipper,

ribbon and bias tape, then walked to Strawberry Way,
where Pa waited and dozed under a *No Parking* sign,
trying to keep an eye out for the police.

GERRY ROSELLA BOCCELLA

A Promise To My Father

Don't ever give our bedroom set away.
We bought it brand new when you were born.
Promise me you'll keep it in the family.

Bed, dresser, armoire, cedar chest, vanity and bench
with original pink upholstered seat just like new.
My mother kept it covered all that time.

Two-toned wood, matching grains with raised designs
in gold and sage green, stylized gilded bows for drawer pulls.
Top-of-the-line thirties design.

I knelt at that bed for all those years to pray for strength,
good health for my family and when the time came, that
I should die in my sleep, he said.

When my father's customers couldn't pay for ice and coal,
they gave him used furniture in return. Their children's
outgrown books, bikes, dolls and wind-up toys.

My job on cleaning day was to carefully remove
Jesus, Mary, vigil light and cut-work scarves before dusting
the dresser with a flannel cloth.

Until the week before he died, I never knew that having
something new, not bartered, meant so much to him.
Or that every night my father knelt to pray.

Let Loose the Reins: A Story of Trust, Strength, and Finding Cows in a Storm

The loud, harsh cracking of tree branches screams through the night. Startled out of a dreamless sleep I open my eyes to darkness. I hear a quick, loud knock on my door. The lights switch on, and my father rushes toward me, his green eyes flicker.

"Dorit, get up, hurry!"

I throw on jeans and a sweatshirt, run to the entry room, pull on my rubber boots, grab a warm jacket and race to the barn. As a 15-year-old farm girl I know where to head in a storm. I lean into the wind, fighting the gusts that toss me sideways. Rain lashes into my face. I hear the heavy branch of a chestnut tree crashing onto the roof. In front of the illuminated entrance to the barn, shingles tumble to the ground and burst into pieces.

My father, a tall man with black hair, a full beard and broad shoulders, guides my five-year-old silver-gray mare, Estella, out of the stable. His calm hand slides the bridle onto her head. Temperamentally, she pushes her nose forward. He instructs me:

"The cows are in danger and I am afraid they'll seek shelter beneath the poplars that will snap like twigs in the storm. We have to find them and bring them home."

My father's strong arms lift me onto the mare's bare back. "Trust your horse," he says, "let the reins loose. Estella will guide you to the cows." He claps my horse on the rear and we're off.

I feel the strength of my mare underneath me. I press my legs into her flanks, urging her forward. Darkness surrounds us. The wind pulls at my hair. Storm clouds race across the sky. The thunder cracks and echoes over the plains of Germany's Lower Rhine Valley as I guide my horse toward the levee. Her secure steps on the muddy ground give me confidence. I have never ridden her at night or in a storm, but I am not afraid. As we reach the top of the earthen dam, I sense the vast meadow that opens up in front of us. Lightning flashes and for a moment the land around unfolds. The Rhine River, a silver stream, reflects the lightning. The poplars jerk back and forth to my far right. They are too distant to see the cows. Then everything returns to darkness. I hear my father's words: "Trust your horse. Let the reins loose."

I push my mare forward. I do not direct her where, but allow her to find her own way. She moves slightly to the right and steps carefully down the levee. I stroke and caress her wet mane. Heavy rain pours down on us. I feel the rhythm of my breath synchronize with hers. I am strong and confident amid the fury of the fall season storm. We find the herd at the outermost edge of the meadow huddled underneath the poplars.

I call the cows, press Estella into a trot and clap my hands. Thirty-five animals start moving. I sense their nervousness. They low and moan loudly. We move up the levee and I hear tree branches snap. Lighting flashes reveal the silhouette of my father, racing towards us. He catches up and together we bring the cows back home to safety.

While my father secures the cows, I guide my horse into the barn, jump off, and grab a towel to dry her fur. Estella turns her head and I see my dad enter the barn.

Then my father, a man who rarely shows emotion, looks into my eyes and says:

"Good job."

I feel his love stream into my heart. I nod, then turn and continue to dry off my horse.

Sunset Turns

You would think they were flamingoes
how they glimmered rose and took their
turns to rise—float—
wings flapping in the setting sun—
before diving for minnows, silver and shimmering
in the backlit air.
But truly they were terns,
dancing just two abreast over pink/purple waves
first one, then the other,
gulping its last sliver of sinew,
as its mate took the plunge
to dive through depths
and crash anew amidst a final glimpse of dusk.
Then, hovering one more time,
evanescent they rose
as they turned north towards their own big dipper
slipping, silent, into the twilight stars.

JUDITH A. BRICE

Clayton 2005

To see the things the old Fricks left,
my sister and I, middle-aged,
middle-class black women
sans the Sunday church hats,
dress up to visit Clayton,
their Point Breeze starter home.
We're pilgrims
to the silver-plated comb,
burnished bronze finger bowl,
totem hunt-scene tapestry—
crystal stations on a rosary
through which the docent leads,
an imagistic communion with a gilded past.
From my sister's slender wrist,
the baffling jingle of tinny bangles
can almost be heard.
Left by an Aunt,
she didn't have much:
the enameled panther knick knacks
linked by gold-tone chain, striding
on the wood-grain coffee table;
above her bed, the plaster crucifix,
its patina of dust;
the R.N.'s uniform,
the heavy woolen cloak worn
on cool nights
for the streetcar ride to the V.A.;
the public workers' pension;
eleven to seven, seven to three, three to eleven,
for thirty years.

The world is a beautiful place

after Ferlinghetti

in early Spring when the squatters come: the tiny bees
embedded in the pillowed pear blossoms,
the sparrows toting twisted curlicues of twig,
making nests under the awning over the deck,
in the dried floral wreath at the door,
under the grill tarp, doing their doo;
their restless chatter, tribal talk,
songs of morning, communal murmurs.
The world is a beautiful place
when it's Monday, but I don't have to leave
the house, and no one is coming to disturb my peace.
When Coco is hopping like a wind-up toy,
barking to the doorbell ringing,
and it's UPS with the book.
When I eat take-out Chinese
and triple-layered mint brownie.
When Satchmo, from the radio (his raspy bass)
calls back the generations: It's 1968 again,
and Mary is seven or eight or ten making
mint-garnished mud pies in the garden
on Lockhart Place. Maxine is complaining
about straightening the bangs
that Mary's dirty fingers ruin
as soon as Maxine turns away.
I'm standing at the back door laughing
at Maxine, her boyish figure, up one side, down
the other, the scowl devouring her peanut face.
The world is a beautiful place
in the summer when the open windows
fill the room with the outdoors,
and dust makes a little tunnel
through the air, pointing the way.

DORALEE BROOKS

Castle Ruins in Alvito

I send a prayer up with the lizard

up the rounded corner turrets

of the 15th century fortress

in my father's hometown,

through the slits for bows and arrows,

where my child father played king and war.

My head cranes back as if to open

my throat to a mother bird.

Duke of Lizards,

where shall I bury him? What shall I do

with his house? What does history say

about the owners of houses,

the recorders of deeds,

the proper distance

to cemeteries?

No Sorry

My mother

lonely in America at 27

pulled me to her collarbone

and asked forgiveness

when I was in second grade

She didn't know I needed gym shorts

and rubber-soled shoes

that I'd have to run

the length of the court

in my dress and socks

I should have told her

other kids did the same as me

I was not alone

DANIELA BUCCILLI

Ariadne Taken

She sleeps wide-eyed
in the rough white box,
seeing only flecks of rocks
in ocean waves.
She is as yet unwashed in wine;
she wears a thin tight slip of light,
transparent as a shade.

His eyes burn through the wall;
she flinches, limbs thrashing,
a lightning-struck doll.
Her fingers rip Olympus;
her toes grip Hades.
The god inside her shatters
before her frenzy fades.

Meteor Lovers

Stars tumble
out of their skulls.
Broken rock circles
clatter through space
on metal chime wings.
Powder silk ghosts
plummet to earth
shimmering green
silt in their eyes
stepping on rusty nails.
They grasp
fiery blue marbles,
juggling them
into a dream
of crawling to
a gray stone cottage
straining towards
an ivory door knob.

JENNIFER BURNAU

To the Little Boy in the White Gown

There's a picture from your christening:
your tiny, red face is bright against the white
gown. I'm wearing my rosebud dress and the
biggest scowl my round, pink face could muster.

I Imagine Death

I imagine death as a boa constrictor, it ties a knot in his neck:
my father fights, maybe howls,
his mouth is a funnel taking this in,
he starts to dicker,
I can't leave, I need to take care of my wife.

Over the spooning of pond-scum lasagna,
had he heard me say, *Don't worry,*
we'll take care of Mom—

had he heard,
that moment his hand dropped into my lap?

In death his mouth refused to close
but we listened, and no one spoke it or knew.

The hole in the world is a banshee's roar.
His limbs   such small sticks.

Night Swallowing

Night swallows leaves with a python throat

Old moon, prune-lipped spinner of cycles
: shaver of skin / knotter of vein :
time cracks in your steel light.

Odd-eyed face in a scarf of cloud, how do you blithely watch and wait?

Snapped fingers of bamboo rake twist from the metal coil
            brushing at life under tufts of browning grass
        and what stays alive in it?

Ant / wooly worm / earwig / grub /
tectonic creak and groan,
fat-bodied insect, *You, old moon*,
you light the dry earth crust,
                        so I ask again,
            what might the horned nail rake apart?
Slug   snail   beetle   larva
pebble / dry shingle scrap / the yard man's cigarette butt

      salt of my late sweat

An Excerpt from *Aquarian Moon*

A white powdered fog suffocates me into a dream, dancing the two-step through my heart and bloating my pupils. I try to press my eyelids open but the fog is too heavy. I need to see—something is not right.

It feels like dew is pasted to my forehead but I know I am in my own bed. Spiders are crawling up my throat and tying webs around my tongue. I try to spit them out, but my body is not cooperating. Instead they continue into my head and scratch at my brain.

My eyes press against the fog and open just enough to make out a figure next to me, but I swear I can see the world turning and I immediately squeeze them shut.

As the spiders clear, questions emerge. How did I get here? What happened last night? I knew if I went searching I would find what I was looking for, but I wasn't really sure I wanted to know.

But I know I have to. I have done something I shouldn't have. I feel it. So I trace back the lines in my memory like retracing the drawing on an Etch A Sketch to find how this all began.

Hey.

Hey, he returns.

Wanna hang out? I ask, trying not to sound desperate.

Sure, me and Con are going to Deli Co. You can come if you want.

Will Heather be there?

Nope.

Good, then I'll see you soon.

No. No. No. This is not the beginning. Why would I have called *him*? What was I thinking? I have to go back further.

This time I see myself sitting in a car. Rain splashes onto my windshield in the light of a street lamp. It makes the glass look like its own black sky; the raindrops are tiny stars sparkling, then melting away. Lots of stars tonight but no moon.

There is not much more detail in this image. There is yelling; words thrown from mouths. "Shut the fuck up!" I hear. The anger is blinding. Our mouths are like windows sifting only hateful words through their panes.

I am sitting in the passenger seat of Matt's car and I am yelling. I cannot hear what I am saying now, but it does not really matter. All these fights are the same. They start simple enough—just me, wanting validation for my feelings. *Don't you see why I'm angry you didn't come home until 4 a.m.? Don't you understand I hate being in the apartment alone? Don't you appreciate that I cleaned up, paid your parking ticket, called you in late to work?* And when there is no validation—there is only flaming anger, and then spinning wheels, and then lots and lots of drinking.

I wanted to force him to understand the way I felt—the pain his leaving caused me, the disappointment in his lack of effort, and the confusion that surrounded every thought I had about us. I wanted to tell him all of it—about the sky on my windshield—but he switches on the wipers, presses his foot to the gas shouting that he'll see me in a few days and drives away, leaving me cold and wet on the sidewalk.

I walk inside our apartment, alone. I need someone to talk to. I wish I could call Kady, Molly, even Lizzy, but I can't. I pick up the phone and do what I know I should not. I call my ex.

When I get to the bar, JB and Con are already playing pool. Neither of them smiles as I enter the room, which gives the night an awkward start. I decide their look of indifference to my presence is an attempt to *be cool* and I brush it off.

"Hey, guys. Are we playing partners or singles? Can I jump in?" I ask.

"Put your quarters up," JB says coolly.

"Dude, what's up? If you didn't want me here, why did you invite me?"

"You called me, remember?" he says, not even looking up from the pool table.

"Right," I mumble.

JB tries to strut smoothly around the pool table like he's the man. He lets his hair fall in his eyes like some Jim Beam model as he leans forward to shoot. He's got a cocky look in his eyes that says to me, *I just got my master's in engineering and am about to make lots of money.* I do my best to flare my nostrils, turn up my lips, and say with my eyes—*nobody cares you arrogant bastard.*

I need a drink.

When I return from the bar, JB offers me a Valium, which I happily swallow with my Captain and ginger.

"You know you miss me," he says with his deep voice less than an inch from my face.

"Hmm, sometimes," I flirt back. I stare into his electric eyes without blinking. I think about pushing his thick, brown hair behind his ear but this is not my job anymore.

My defenses are slowly coming down. If Matt knew I was here, getting wasted with my ex, he'd be furious and that's exactly the way I wanted it. JB puts Widespread Panic's *Climb to Safety* on the jukebox, the Valium kicks in, and my night instantly takes a wonderful turn—I smile easily and dance freely around the pool table, spinning and allowing the music to wrap around me like a spool of thread.

When JB asks me to come over to his apartment, I do not even need to think about it.

Harwood Museum: Modern Art Exhibit

I
this empty noose
has been blingalized
full of rhinestone shine

this is art
hanging here
in a room for exhibition

this empty noose
shards of glass and glit
sparkle against abstract black

this empty oblong head
is full of mob method:
burn flesh, eat it
rare

this starry night
pulled bone by bone
is split from heavenly body

II
I have watched
my mother polish silver
rich folk forks, knives

blades so bright
rage flays the tongue
as two fish flop

fillet—no water, silent
as a pine tree's arm
when I carve

a heart on its skin
art of true love.

SHEILA L. CARTER-JONES

A Room with Better Lighting (A Novel Excerpt)

After we cleaned up the kitchen, Ruby said she wanted to show Eddie and Joelle our garden. "You won't believe it, we have the biggest tomato plants in the whole world. Tell 'em Iris."

"We do. You just won't believe it," I said. Ruby and I led the way out the back door with big smiles, our arms spread out wide, palms up, like the ladies on the game shows.

Eddie stood on the back stoop and looked at the garden with this queer look on his face, then back at Ruby and me, smiling. He walked over to a tomato plant, then another, looking real hard, like he'd never seen one before. He broke off a big leaf and smelled it, then another. Then he just busted out laughing. Ruby asked him what was so darn funny. He was bent over heaving so hard he couldn't talk. He tried, but all he could get out was, "Sorry, Mama" and then he'd start laughing again. Ruby and I didn't know what to make of it, Joelle either.

Joelle went over to Eddie and looked real close at the plants, too, then Eddie whispered something to her and she started laughing like him, like it was contagious or something.

Ruby put her hands on her hips. "Why are y'all laughin' at our tomato plants?" This just made 'em laugh even more.

Joelle said, "Ruby, honey, these aren't tomato plants."

Uncle Eddie was almost crying now. "Mama, what you have here is the most beautiful crop I've ever seen in my whole life. Of marijuana."

Ruby started to swoon. I pulled her lawn chair over just in time. Then it hit me. "That bag of seeds and stuff you found in the refrigerator after the cop took Eddie away last time, remember? You were so mad you just threw that bag out the back door, remember, Ruby?" Her eyes darted back and forth. I handed her a sweet grass fan and she started swishing it. It was coming back to her now.

Eddie and Joelle composed themselves but couldn't help some busting up again. Ruby didn't see the humor. She was mad. She started to stand up, then thought better of it. "Okay, since you two know so much about marijuana, I want you to pull up every one of those plants. Iris, run inside and get a couple of trash bags for them. Then you come here by me, child—you're not touching a one of those illegal plants. Y'hear?"

"Yes, Ma'am."

Eddie and Joelle started yanking up those marijuana plants with Ruby overseeing the whole thing, sitting tall in her chair, like a prison guard over a chain gang.

Then I remembered, "Jesus, Mary and St. Joseph! We gave marijuana plants to all the neighbors!"

Ruby fainted.

That night, all four of us, dressed in dark clothes, crept into the neighbors' yards, each with a flashlight and trash bag. Ruby and I had to go, too, since we knew the lay of the land, the local dogs, and where the "tomato" plants were. Mrs. Blake had two plants. Ruby said one was a volunteer. Mr. Thomas had the worst green thumb this side of Mississippi because his plant was all dried up and shriveled.

Floyd Whipple, the caretaker, was our last stop. He sure was an odd duck. Ruby said it always made her feel good when she worked late, knowin' Mr. Whipple was sittin' out underneath his old oak tree, just in case I ever needed anything. I didn't have the heart to tell her he was a pervert. The time I came over to bring Ruby's special peach cobbler, I caught him looking at girlie magazines underneath that big old oak, just out of Mrs. Whipple's sight.

We looked under the oak now, to make sure he wasn't sitting there. It was pitch black. We could barely see. Joelle shined the light into the yard. He wasn't there, but he had a big dog, Festus, and a fence. Ruby told Eddie to go in and told him where to look while we waited.

Bang! It sounded like a shotgun. Every light inside Mr. Whipple's house and all the outside security lights went on, and I saw Mr. Whipple let Festus loose out the back door. We could see Eddie running and Festus right on his heels, barking like crazy. Eddie musta had a lot of practice jumping fences, 'cause he jumped that one running, and we all ran home, closed the door, and fell into a heap on the mudroom floor.

My heart pounded, and I could hear Eddie's too. He looked at me and smiled. I put my arms around him and Joelle and reached over to pat Ruby, "Wasn't that fun, everybody?"

Ruby said, "Iris, you be quiet."

"Oh, let her go, Mama," said Eddie. "She's just excited."

"I sure am—this is the best, most fun night I've ever had in my whole life. Wow," I said. For some reason, Eddie thought that was funny. He started laughing, then Joelle, then Ruby, all of them laughing at me, but I didn't care, I was just happy to be there, with them.

Since it was so late, Ruby talked Joelle into spending the night. I slept on the couch. The next morning when I woke up, Eddie was already gone and you know what? For the first time ever, he didn't take anything. This time he left something. It was a diary, not my old one that he stole last time and I still missed, but a brand new one, the prettiest diary I'd ever seen. It had a lock with a gold key. There was a receipt in it from the prison gift shop that said it cost three dollars. I left the receipt on the counter, where Ruby was sure to see it. I figured it would make her real proud, it being proof and all that Eddie didn't steal it. He'd bought it...for me.

Late Autumn on the Allegheny

It is so quiet out on the river now—
the jarring noises of summertime
boats and people falling into silence.
All but the last crinkled, yellowed leaves
have drifted down from the island's trees,
and only a few hardy ducks remain.
Even the Great Blues are lying low,
waiting, watching, eager to sleep away
the winter under marbled-gray skies.

Waves lap upon the russet shoreline
as a gentle breeze ruffles the water.
This is the stark season when Nature
goes underground.

Paperwhites

They are blooming in the corner
by my window, exotic fragrance
strong in the undiluted sunlight.
I want to bathe in their perfume,
and float in their fragile beauty.
Early harbingers of spring, though
I have brutally forced their flowering
from ugly dormant brown bulbs,
they give me some hope that winter
won't last forever and that I, too,
will find a way to bloom again.

I just want to kiss

I remember the first time—
a kiss
me kissing   a woman

I knew

There was no discussion
of head tilts or eyes open
only desires   drawn together

Teeth touched   Lips lingered

Tongues teased

A slow departure
made me blink

With finger tip
I touched
my own disbelief

So different, from kissing
the back of my hand
the chill of the mirror
the placement of my pillow.

So different
from the childhood stories
the taunts and teasing

CJ COLEMAN

I knew
there was life
behind this love
I was   in love

I loved
that very first kiss

1971

when I was seven
my mother taught me
how to make a bed with
hospital corners

taught me how to smooth
the sheets
from top to bottom

to be sure to pull the top sheet
tight,
tuck it under at the bottom
and make the folds crisp
like angles
on both sides

I watched
and thought the bed looked
like the box corners of
foil wrapped gifts
she'd given me at Christmas

we went room to room that morning
until all seven beds were done
and I asked my mother why

why she needed to show me
how to make a bed look

she said   *just in case*

CJ COLEMAN

just in case I ever had to
make a white woman's
bed someday

I'd be ready

Jimmy Harr's Ford Fairlane

On our way to burgers and shakes after the game
we crammed eight kids into the car,
stopped at my house to get
permission for me to go.

My father came out to the car to talk to Jimmy:
How long have you been driving?
How old are you?
Did you ever get a ticket for speeding?

This car will do 120, he said and leaned
into the open window to look at us, smelled
Jimmy's breath for booze. *My dad will take away my keys*
if I speed, Jimmy lied. I held my breath. Jimmy

was a smart ass. He worked at his dad's Ford
dealership, loved cars. After my dad
was out of ear shot, Jimmy joked
I didn't tell him I got this car cheap

because it conks out at 80. Everyone laughed.
We pulled away. Out the back window
I watched my dad brush the stones from his socks
before he went back into the house.

KAY COMINI

The Last Strip of Siding

The Japanese knotweed in the vacant lot has grown
to 12 feet over summer. It is yellow now, edges

curling brown. On the other side of the Earth,
tsunamis, volcanoes. But here in Pittsburgh

the sky is grey. Clouds pillow against each other
in shades of oyster, slate, dove. Halloween weather.

The sumac blazes red. Two pigeons on the chimney cap
fattened for winter, fluffed up in the cold. Smoke

from the asphalt factory under the Birmingham Bridge
rises straight up, just beyond the yellow crane lifting I beams.

My neighbor has nailed the last strip of siding
to his house. Put up storm windows. I got out

the new flannel sheets, retrieved the down comforter
from the cupboard under the window.

The lawn furniture has been covered; wind chimes
taken down and hung in the basement.

Me and Mary Weidner

snicker about her chicken pictures.
They began in an open-air market
in Montmartre. She snapped photos
of the Eiffel Tower, Notre Dame,
then slipped around a corner and found
plucked chickens and turkeys dangling,
lined up, piled up for purchase.
The artist knows when she trips upon her subject.
Les Poulets Parisiennes were born
on film, in oil, watercolor, pencil.
She knows they won't sell, these sensuous
but something-more-than-naked chickens.
They resemble human body parts,
skin like yours or mine, not fowl.
Curves suggest people's private parts.
Is that obscene? my naïve self asks.
She says, *You could interpret it that way.*

ANN CURRAN

The bottle blonde

with Wonder Bread breasts

leans over

taps my arm.

"What's your name?

I want to pray for you."

Pray for the kids in Somalia

better yet buy them a goat.

I paid fifty bucks to

hear Lucinda Williams sing,

not to be reminded.

You think I should be grateful

thrilled to be bald and 20 pounds heavier.

Just add me to your list and I'm sure

your god will fix everything.

Meanwhile, give yourself a pat on the back

and leave me alone.

Survivor

Still   myself—
hollow but meaty

Sturdy feet
    detour
down tear trails
    slick and salty

Imagine
    a lake
ripples reversed
    rock
returns to hand

Poem w/Canon II

As I prepare for launch, I think of the lines of men
watching, how they are no longer lions for me—
long since I've fucked one, so I embrace the steel phallus,

go inside—never having sex—I think about it
as I crawl into the catapult, adjust the cupola again,
human cannonball, never having sex again—

head tucked, somersaults in the air, screaming yellow
streaming ribbons—fire-breathing eyes,
I soar over motorcycle men in spandex—

swinging trapeze artists, clowns with painted-on smiles,
the ringmaster with his all-American looks—
pink cotton candy as I hit the net.

Pyrotechnics

I jump from a burning building,
the Dwarf dressed like a baby in diapers, and a bonnet,
he's wailing, while I push him aside to save my own life,
falling down three stories where clown-faced firemen
stand ready, hold the safety net.

In Clown School, we all got our pyrotechnics license,
our black powder, our Saran Wrap, some electrical tape
and a squib—knowledge second to none. (Bet your powder sock,
you can set your sleeves on fire if you're not careful.)

Randy Costello rigs Lou Jacob's little car and between shows
we hear a familiar whoosh, smell gunpowder. Randy screams
son of a bitch—(What a nasty habit he has, forgetting to disconnect
the batteries before connecting the squibs.)

Those were the days—Zapata's run-in with the long rifle,
Jimmy Briscoe's flash powder party surprise, Tedrick juggling
flaming torches. Dana & Max's *smoking* costumes!
Just the other day, I had the itch to make a cigarette bomb.
Good thing I've quit smoking.

From the Canal

It wanted to explode me, it wanted to break my fucking neck—
but my head had stopped swimming, bursting like a bulb
from bloody water. Then my slippery shoulders. I wanted
my whole body through, but it caught at the hip, popping
the long bone from its socket. Making me cripple for a year.
Forcing a flowering fuse through my green brain. Firing
all synapses for *legs* into howls. Words became my crawl,
my stuttering strokes from the canal when they lifted me,
and I swear I understood them despite their white masks,
opening silted eyes to the light of a thousand tongues.

Sunflowers in October

grow even on Penn Avenue
a line drawn in sandy Garfield dirt.
Something cocky in their raised faces
something frozen
saffron glad-rag spikes
stiff on thin browned stems.
They endure
for a brief generation—
brazen backs
against walls of sooty brick
against boarded windows
blank as schoolrooms
against plate-glass galleries
pristine as shrink-wrapped plastic.
Whussup?
Live sap hardens to a pose
for sentinels who craved a piece of sky
hard and bright as a passing jet
exhaust
streaming needle-sharp
fading too fast.
Whussup, man?
What carrion crows strip their seeds
to faces hollow as scraped pans of batter
knowing one law—
nothing fertile but your concrete self.

ANGELE ELLIS

Stopping for the Dead

I have a friend who stops for dead
cats in the road, to check their vitals
just in case.

My friend still believes in miracles.

Some people think she is crazy,
for touching the little bodies
left to rot on the double yellow lines—

sad, we think we are the only creatures
who deserve respect in death.

Once on the downtown bus,
I overheard a woman whisper
about her dogs:

"I think he knows the other is dead"

I used to sleep with a man who owned guns.
He used them to shoot the deer he fed
corn and apples to all summer long.

I thought it was so strange
to make friends with something you cleaned
your gun for.

He took me into the woods in December
snow. I couldn't feel my ass,
wished I had a book.

I got into trouble for making noise,
for breaking twigs,
and was glad he missed.

When we were kids,
I always made my sister gut the trout
during fishing trips with our father.

The scales, iridescent gasoline,
too beautiful for me to pierce.
The hidden orange eggs
too much for me to see
mixed in with the dirt.

CALEY FERGUSON

Waiting for a Funeral at the Holiday Inn Express on Route 30

I.
The way a brother comforts a sister:
I found you some weed.

Stuff some towels under the bathroom door. Turn on
the fan and the shower. Burn the end of a joint with
flimsy hotel matches. Inhale. Exhale. Cough.

It's okay to get high when your
heart is broken.

II.
The way believers understand death:
God needed her in Heaven more than
we needed her on Earth.

*The Lord gave, and the Lord hath taken away; blessed be the name of
the Lord.*

It's okay to be selfish when you're sovereign.

III.
The way neighbors say they are sorry:
Mashed potatoes with brown gravy, crispy
chicken thighs, orange-yellow cheesy casseroles.

Have another Budweiser to wash down the sixth chocolate cupcake.
Peel the fried skin from a piece of chicken. Eat it. Repeat.

It's okay to get fat if your grandmother is dead.

Don't forget the chipped ham smothered
in watery barbeque sauce, store bought cole slaw,
St. Patrick's Day doughnuts, and the boxed wine.

IV.
The way a mortician prepares for a funeral:
Log the dead's jewelry. Report any bruising
or discoloration. Spray the skin, eyes, and mouth
with disinfectant. Shave the face.

Place pieces of cotton over the sunken eyeballs.
Glue the eye lids shut. Use a curved hook
to close the mouth with string. Make the smile
pleasant.

It's okay to cry if you knew the dead.

Drain the blood. Pump two gallons
of chemicals into veins and tissue.
Suck decaying fluid from leftover organs.
Pack cotton in the anus and vagina to prevent
seepage.

Wash, dry, and brush the hair. Put a
favorite blue sweater on the body.
Smooth thick make-up over the face,
neck and hands.

Cover the black forehead bruise with concealer.
Apply black mascara, shimmering pearl eye shadow,
and frosty pink lipstick to the mouth.

V.
The way Catholics celebrate Lent:
An extra day of penance is mandatory if
meat is consumed on Fridays even during
post-funeral luncheons at small fire halls.

Remember, Jesus bled like an undercooked hamburger for our sins.

*For us men and our salvation He came down from heaven: by the power
of the Holy Spirit, He was born of the Virgin Mary, and became man.
For our sake He was crucified under Pontius Pilate; He suffered, died,
and was buried.*

It's okay to order the jumbo shrimp cocktail as an appetizer.
Squeeze extra lemon juice on their chilled bodies. Hold them
by the tail. Drag them through spicy cocktail sauce.

Blessed be the name of the Lord.

Crossing

Our ship cuts sleekly into the water, sudsing it enough that the turquoise bleeds through. The sun and sea work together to bring out the aqua. We rarely see indigo, a lively deep blue, some say our spirit color. When we pass through the Baltic, an evanescent band of violet glows at sundown. This far north the sunsets hold onto us for hours to make up for that thief, winter—the long dark cold when one must look for color in the ice. Or look through welders' glass to see the sun's corona. When there *is* sun. But at this time of year, that golden orb dallies for hours like electric pudding on the ocean's edge till our eyes tear.

Mostly, the Atlantic is battle gray, like the sky. Often, depending where we are, the fog sneaks in—one minute the sky, the next minute an opaque reflection that works its way into us. The ship slows. Then the foghorn bays every two minutes—international law—forlorn but somehow comforting. The water makes hushing sounds. Through the night, I walk the Promenade Deck, and it feels like I'm walking to nowhere.

The next day, a tiny sailboat is eaten up by the horizon. Sailors are the only ones unfailingly attuned to how wind walks on water—or runs, charges. Every second counts when manning the sails. But we're not on a sailboat.

Birds glide close to the waves with no place to sleep but the water. They don't trust our ship, just as they don't trust the back of a whale. They glide on the updraft from waves for thousands of miles—millions really, if we count a life span of thirty years, some of them reaching Antarctica only to nest. These, the whales and porpoises, and an occasional flying fish are our only companions. Sometimes for days we don't see another boat or a bird.

Sometimes, when clouds sag gray against the horizon, the Atlantic is dirty green, which speaks oddly of life: if we blink, we might miss it. Any minute the sky can change. Any minute the sea might dream up a gale. And if we were in that small sailboat...?

ALICE FUCHS

But lo! how the white sun sinks into a sea of diamonds.

In a tempest, the ship's skeleton groans and creaks. The wind whistles, shrieks. The boat has weathered many storms—even once, in the South Pacific, a rogue wave. The captain watched his coffee leave the cup, then drop back into it. He tells us this because he wants us to feel safe. He's still here, we see.

The ship allows us to see the waves up close. We can be dining while in the trough of a twenty-foot swell. We can be ducking from flatware shearing across the dining room, or hear, behind us, a horrendous crash as a waiter drops his tray of dishes so he can rescue an old woman who's falling. He becomes a hero. He sings and dances. He tells us he's seen worse. He tells us sometimes the windows break.

But that's why we're here—partly for the thrill. Partly to tell stories: at sea we tell stories; on shore we tell stories. Why should everything happen to other people?

I love the sea.

My favorite photo of me is my *Old Man and the Sea* spread open on my lap, beyond it my legs and feet, then the railing and the sea. I took it myself.

Ahoy! Another small sailboat, the size of my bed. It can't be the same one. And there's land! It's County Cork, Ireland— emerald green nestling atop chalk cliffs. How hungry we are for this green. One lone lighthouse. Then the Irish! I want to hug every one of them, throw back a pint in the nearest pub. Taste their scones. Not as cosmic as the sea, at first glance. But then, I only have to look deep enough.

At Home

I have a home.   This is my home.

The leaky faucet's drip, drip. My roommate's hard rock music in the other room.

A few moments ago, I sat in our main room, staring up at the two pictures of flying pigs hanging above our bunk beds. Havilah and I named them Adalbert (he's the older, for the name is befitting) and Ingomar (the younger succinctly).

I stare up at the spider hanging out on the window ledge. He's been mocking me for days on end simply by moving his miniscule body a few inches up or down every day.

I glance over at the stack of washed dishes waiting patiently to be dried and put in their proper place.

I have a home.   This is my home.   I prefer it to any other home.

LAUREN GAULT

The Salon

For some reason
I am reminded
of you in all this:

       this cutting and chattering
         the brushing and blowing
           and pulling and plying
         this talk of wild turkeys
            another holiday
        and all these mirrors.

Things here are made
to do what they won't
if left untouched,
then sprayed to last
well past
coffee, mincemeat,

          all these mirrors
        and these reflections
           of reflections
             of you
              me
            out past

the other side
of
everything.

Tearing Down the House: Anorexia Unfettered

I am the weight of this hunger.
Its multiple bodies pulse inside me:
I am the starving dog, wailing infant,
lost exile, forlorn teen.

I am the parrot plucking her own feathers
from a bloodied chest.
Battered child, betrayed friend,
disowned daughter, numbed-out whore.

Bear in a steel trap eating
its paw to free its leg.
Body tortured by its internal fire.
I starve, stuff, gag, nauseate,

mutilate my voracious body.
I walk your backroads when you sleep,
slit open your dreams and enter.
I unlock the secret space in your house,

loose the bats.

MARLENE GOLDSMITH

hydrangea and free fall

I envied that luscious burst of bubble-flower, cellular profusion
that defies constraint and I was reminded of that little girl in the

aqua dress jumping off the porch step in free fall, head thrown
back, arms out-stretched, reaching for the sky in full confidence

that the brick path would be there when she landed and my father
aiming his Rolleiflex, *Smile now, honey, hold still,* even as I floated

free in space I just knew I owned.

Some days I am

soft silk and shimmery satin, delicate
trochees sitting lightly on the page

hard leather with gold studs, jackboots
storming citadels, firing brilliant ideas
from this Glock brain, stunning

warmed by the fire in my belly
spelling myself on the page

struggling to find

skipping along the strand, sloshing
through surf, abandoning

plunging into the brilliant dark,
getting the blood and fuck down on paper,
showing the body

wet with wanting, aching for my lost
lover when words were irrelevant

some nights just whispers and cries.

LOIS I. GREENBERG

I Walk

I approach the three-way stop where my walking route turns right and down a steep slope. The descent strengthens the front of my meniscus-threatened right knee and leads to a long circular upward climb that hardens my back and thigh muscles, taking pumping stress from my aging heart. I think in those terms out here. As I place one foot ahead of the other, I walk with a chorus of voices I will no longer hear and faces whose recalled images have blurred with time. I carry the genetic seeds that took them away too soon. And so, I walk with the hope that I can out-distance their early fate.

Walking has been my salvation. Twenty-plus years ago my physician became concerned over test result changes from the previous year. Prescriptions were written, diet changes were outlined, but his most valuable advice was the suggestion that I walk several miles every day. I bought a new pair of shoes for the assignment and began the habit that has changed and enriched my life.

Home is in the southwest corner of Pittsburgh, tucked between a tony 1930's borough and a sprawling, semi-rural independent municipality. While enjoying quiet, less traveled streets, my borough lacks sidewalks, so I hit my initial strides on the better-paved neighboring byways. As I gained in physical strength and attained better results at my check-ups, the steeper, more challenging hills on my own turf beckoned and I shifted my trek to a two-and-a-half-mile loop of asphalt, sans sidewalks, that meanders from my address and leads me through a pleasant 1950's, ranch-house era neighborhood.

Over the years, my quiet odyssey and the time it affords me for reflection has remained one of the few constants in the changing inner landscape that inevitably accompanies growing older. I have witnessed the arrival of new homeowners, new puppies, and new babies. I have learned pets' names—Oreo,

Dakota, Coby; watched them gain discipline, grow old and eventually be replaced with a new arrival. I've overheard awkward teenagers angrily protesting the unfairness of their chores, waved at them as they took their first solo drive in the family car, and revisited my own memories as they posed for prom pictures in front of a flowering shrub. Mature versions of those same teens have recently greeted me, babies in tow.

I watch the unexplained neglect of a normally well-groomed property that signals change. Soon the lawn sprouts signs: "Moving Sale," "Estate Sale," "For Sale;" the sturdy realty post appears, shouting its names and numbers. The ebb and flow of a life has taken a new turn.

It's an early mid-summer morning. I have to beat the heat of the rising sun, which even now bores down on my back as I lean into the return side of this ridge and cross over into the shady lane that leads to home. This is Thursday. I would know that without a calendar, for it is trash day. Each lawn is edged by lumpy green offerings for the noisy monster-truck that gobbles up the weekly cast-offs from our plenty. Two of those plastic bags sit plopped at the edge of the lawn facing the intersection where I turn. There had been an orange and white U-Haul in the driveway for the past two mornings. The bags are punctured here and there and broken toys are recognizable inside one gash. The family hadn't lived here a full year and the probable pain of their departure spoke to my heart.

The next morning I leave home even earlier. The heat had neared three digits yesterday and that last climb had been a challenge. As I arrive at the three-way, I notice a small silvery plastic sword that lay trapped in a cooled puddle of tar where the torn bags had sat the previous day. The remarkable precision of the miniature extruded shape catches my attention. It is complete with a braided hilt and well-proportioned blade. I muse on how many minds would have worked together to produce such a seemingly insignificant little object.

"Good morning, little memory," I smile at my recall of little fingers bristling with similar armor those few short years before. With the already encroaching heat, I know the tiny reminder will be short-lived in his black showcase; soon to be carried away in a tire tread.

The little sword is still there the next day.

Remarkably, it remains; somehow evading the notice of curious new tenants in the little house, torrential summer rains and winter snow plows. That insignificant two-and-a-half-inch piece of plastic steadfastly occupies its now-dull tarry frame for four years.

Early this spring, a mother and several children stop at the intersection as I approach. The mother is readjusting two babies in a large stroller. Several toddlers and school-age children mill around the space. I catch myself feeling torn between being pleased that the little sword might be appreciated as a toy again and sadness at losing a touch point on which I had come to rely. The moment passes. The puppy-tumble of little ones move on and when I get to the intersection, there gleams the little sword; undisturbed.

I've become a little obsessed with the sword. After several long vacation absences and stretches of weather too icy for me to safely be out, it continues to greet me from its precarious post—small icon of perseverance; encouragement to keep walking.

Slipper Orchids

Bottom petals like throats
blown open into bubbles—
pelican's full pouch,
fleshy purse
of a double chin,
bullfrog in love.
Gaping pockets
tempt me to hold them
between thumb and forefinger,
to pinch without popping.

AMY LEE HEINLEN

When You Feel Earthbound

Remember the ostrich that cannot fly
her theatrical body of feathers
sweeping as cirrus clouds.
She can race like a horse
but rarely lends her back for a ride.
She, who has been lied about—
knuckle-head in the sand—
has said nothing, jaunty as a Sunday hat.
Her one stunning kick will kill a man,
her wide-eyed downy-headed look
can peck a chuckle at his feet,
lay a laugh in his throat. She
lays eggs big enough to imagine dinosaurs
low in the branches of the family tree,
big enough to support evolution
even in the most fragile of right minds.
Improbable but there she is:
a flightless, giant, deadly bird,
a gawky, long-necked wonderment
to those tiny, soaring, looking down.

When Dinosaurs Ate People

Michael woke with a start and turned his head quickly on the yellowing pillow to see his brother, Danny, crouched, one knee up and one knee down, on the scarred wooden chair. Danny peered over the top of it and out the window. He didn't turn but, looking out, said, "I'm scared."

Michael was the big brother at six. He had to be brave. Danny was only five and wore the jeans he'd slept in. They were too big and skidded down his backside. His t-shirt by contrast was too small and rucked up under his armpits. Both were hand-me-downs. His heavy mop of brown hair made his face seem small. His sad eyes were the same as Michael's, blue. "Aw, we'll be all right, Danny. C'mon, let's just get ready for school." He threw the blanket back from their shared single bed and got out, his legs goose-pimpling from the cold.

Danny watched him dress without leaving his perch. "I'm scared. I don't want to go out there. Those dinosaurs are a hundred feet long. They can do what they want. They can get who they want. They can eat us!"

It had been wrong for Michael to tell Danny that there were dinosaurs around. They'd watched that movie; it had seemed so real. He should probably tell him it wasn't true, but it had been so fun to see his eyes widen and to be the brave hero. He couldn't resist talking about talons reaching out to grab you and teeth filled with gore. He'd said the dinosaurs were moving north and looking for more food, probably coming to where they lived soon. He was so good at scaring Danny that he'd sort of scared himself. Even so he said, "I won't let anything get you, Buddy. I'll protect us."

"But it's not the same now. We could get caught just going to the bus. I think we should just stay here."

Michael looked around at the faded puke green paint, the water stains on the ceiling and warped and darkened wood on the floor. He picked up their shirts while shaking his head. "No, Buddy, c'mere, let me button this shirt on you. If you tuck it in, you can't see the ketchup you got on it yesterday. I know it's not the same, but we'll be okay."

"We can't be okay. We can't do anything about it. We don't have guns. Everything downstairs stinks. They got in; they're here, I'm telling you, we have to stay here. And the worst thing is we can't even watch cartoons."

Michael put his own shirt on. He ran his fingers through his hair and did the same for his brother. They could get the free breakfast at school so long as they didn't miss the bus. He tied his brother's shoes and said, "Remember how I told you. They only notice moving stuff. So walk real slow and quiet and when we get close to the bus, run like crazy, okay?"

Carrying their jackets, they tiptoed down the right-hand side of the steps to avoid the creaking. The smell of urine and fecal matter made the hair on Michael's neck stand up. He watched the entrance of the living room where their Mom had put the old bed for her grandmother. It had been just three days now. They said there was no money for the hospital and she had to be somewhere. So they brought her here. Danny and Michael didn't want to go in there. No one did. They didn't know her. Her wispy hair didn't cover her age-speckled skull, her fingers bent to each other, all huge knots and sharp points, and her missing teeth made her mouth a well hole, collapsing at the edges and black inside. But she hollered and roared when she wanted something, and it seemed like she always wanted something.

Michael cautioned Danny in a whisper, "Remember, go slow and quiet, and when we're close to the bus, we run."

Danny looked back at his brother, "You won't let it get me, right?" Michael shook his head yes, all the while staring hard at the entrance to the living room as they descended and the scene spread out before them, a mustard-colored, unswept carpet, a pressed wood coffee table placed atop the blanket-covered couch, both pushed to the wall, the old box TV in the corner where they couldn't watch it anymore.

He didn't look at the bed; he didn't want to look at the bed. *Please just get by.* They stealthily crossed the hallway from the foot of the steps toward the front door. Danny was just opening it when the old woman screeched.

"Run, Danny, run," whispered Michael, and he turned to face the old dinosaur.

Butler City

We stop at a five-street intersection:
Jefferson Street & Main meet three alleys & a shoulder,
the buildings clash here.
Old city bricks against new development steel—
windows empty with the lack of jobs.
As we pass through on Jefferson, turn on to Pittsburgh Road
& climb to the top of the world.
Hail bounces off the windshield,
clean white against the gray of Butler City,
the empty cornfields of Junction 356.
We pull over & wait.
A doe walks up to the car,
looks us each in the eye, presses her nose to the window
& disappears.
They buy a lot of weed here,
mostly bring it from Beaver or Pittsburgh,
because there's nothing else to do
besides smoke and go bowling,
smoke and go swimming at Days Inn,
smoke and walk around town,
smoke and go to Dollar General & Family Video,
play guitar in the music store,
drive through the country to Renfrew & Old Plank.
When the pickup pulls beside us,
they open the door, we open the window.
He hands us a bag & takes the money.

CHRISTINA M. JELLISON

Hitting It

The key is that everyone realizes there is no magic answer to this.
—R. Gil Kerlikowske, Director White House Office of National Drug Control Policy

The new approach will depend on education, stepped-up law enforcement and pill-tracking databases, with particular emphasis on Florida, where 85 percent of all oxycodone pills in the nation are prescribed. Many of those end up along the East Coast and in Appalachia, where people take buses to Florida just to get pills in a phenomenon dubbed the 'OxyContin Express.'
—Curt Anderson, Associated Press

First Friday of every month
we drive down to St. Augustine,
Welfare slips stuffed in our pockets.
Stop in Captain's Pantry,
buy a pack of Big Red, some Cheetos,
Mountain Dew & get change from a hundred dollar voucher.
We hit up six more stores,
then down the street to the Comfort Care
where *I threw out my back at work &*
yes it hurts to move.
Got my shoulder replaced
six weeks ago & I ran out of my pills.
The physician's assistant on duty in pink scrubs
writes a prescription for 240 oxycontins,
stamps it with the doctor's name.
Out the door & heading back to Pittsburgh
where it's forty dollars a pill &
the kids on the street will pay double.

Dear Hysteria

Ha! You braying loon, eyes
squirming in all directions.
You crack me up! Look
at you, hair teased too high,
blouse buttoned wrong.
In the bedroom, you're bumpin:
You've got your mother in a whirl,
you don't know if you're a boy or a girl.
You've kept me up all night
with your racket. Let's go.
Let's fight dirty.
Let's take it outside.

JILL KHOURY

Ode to the Letter J

Pen to paper,
upsweep
to the down,
a slope, a hook—
in cursive a nook
with places to hide,
or, fidgeting and bored,
to color in.
When I sign,
I range far above
and below
the midline:
emphasizing both
superego and id.
Sometimes just J-period.
It's enough
to say J, the swagger
the claw,
the dagger
tip.

Three Weeks After

Clearer than daybreak, I saw him.
Jack was standing a few yards away from me
in front of the Golden Gate Bridge,
wearing a navy blue sweater that I'd given him
a few Christmases ago.

He was smiling,
a light tan jacket over his arm. He was just
about to turn, and I couldn't stop him.
Couldn't move. Behind him, others were
heading toward the bridge.
It was early fall, a sunny day.

If I could have,
I would have gone up to him
and hugged him, held for a minute
his broad, soft shoulders, as if I could thank him
with that gesture for his soft voice,
pitched just above a whisper.
For being one of three men who ever bought me flowers.
For stopping, for a moment, to say goodbye.

MICHELLE MAHER

Vessel

My fear? That someday I'll die and,
shorn of flesh, I'll rise and march
my gleaming bones to some arid plain
where others, just like me,
skinned next to nothing, will ask each other,

Who are we? Where have we been?
And if this happens I will be very angry.
What I want most is to shake off
my old form, to be scoured clean
like a copper pot or tin basin

worn next to nothing, until one day
the scrubber wears a hole
through a side, so that the vessel
stands empty to a sharp wind,
abandoned, useless, at last

come into its own.
Anything less would be unbearable,
not when the rocks and clouds are free
to move through time unencumbered
by wants and fears.

I will ask death:
take away my fear of being only me.
Let me pour out my life
like a heavy vase filled to the top and then
turned end over end above dry ground.

PA Woman Beats Man with a Frying Pan

*Police in central Pennsylvania say a woman is facing charges after she hit
a man in the head with a large frying pan…the man, whose name wasn't
released, suffered an abrasion on his head.*
—SABC Local News, July 12, 2010

If you had lived in their house
you wouldn't need to ask why,
as she stood at the stove,
worn bathrobe, eyes blank, his voice —

the words having long ago
lost separate shapes, become one droning mass of sound,
reaching out his plate for more, smacking wet lips
between gulps of orange juice.

But why that morning?
Perhaps it was a thought that flitted thin
as the egg's skin she broke over the bowl:
she'd never done this alone, in silence —

always had his yammering cloud of self
waiting, always, to be acknowledged by her
as right / as the man /
as water wears stone
he had chiseled her down.

Perhaps she'd simply never noticed the heft of the pan,
never considered how hard and fast she could swing it,
wondered if he'd see it coming —

if his head would even stop talking
once the hot pan made contact with his ear.
Maybe she thought only of the possibility of silence,
just for a little while —
silence

EMILY MOHN

Your Blade

My cart glides into the frozen foods aisle
and there you are, unloading bags of frozen peas,
ripping apart the box with your blade.

You look good, you say. I return the compliment
(and wish I didn't mean it). We laugh about the time
you slipped and fell trying to moonwalk on our kitchen floor.

I forgot how laughing with you is harder than anything now.
I push my cart away and after a few seconds look over my shoulder.
Your back is foreign. I wonder if anyone has touched it since you left.

Dashed

—from an Associated Press photo, Pittsburgh Post-Gazette, May 19, 2011

In the photo a man is attempting to pull a jilted bride
up from a seventh floor window in Changchun, China.
She's jumped from the window. Minutes ago, the groom
had called off their marriage. The rescuer struggles
to grasp the young woman by her arms. Facing outward,
she leans her head against the building, her black hair
falling over her eyes. Her silky white wedding dress
and see-through veil drift downward in swirling white.
Dainty lace peeks from the edges of her strapless top
and from her hemline, stretched lightly above slender ankles
and delicate shoes. Slim with soft bare shoulders,
she looks fragile as a butterfly. Another man balances
on a windowsill below, and reaches up to grasp her feet.

MARILYN MARSH NOLL

Encounter

A black butterfly wearing
a lacy brown shawl
landed on our impatiens.

Ignoring the reds and pinks,
she flew from one purple
bloom after another

drinking their nectar.
Later I discovered purple
impatiens growing wild

between cracks in our sidewalk.
Careful not to trample them,
I marveled as they thrived.

One day a black butterfly,
edged in brown like the other,
fluttered onto those flowers.

I watched her until—satisfied—
she flew toward me and gently
brushed against my blouse.

Weather Report

Rain today to cool the temper of an overheated world.
Yesterday I put in little shade plants where Bob and I
had dug up evil-smelling underground networks
of chameleon plant spread the way Joe McCarthy thought

communists did, underground, fat, white and sneaky. Moved
a couple of ferns crowded too close to others. Inspected tomatoes
in the sunny front yard, where they are growing tall, yellow
blossoms setting into small green fruit. And cut down, dug up

the white Darlow's Enigma rose that had given way
to its weedier sport. Cleaned the front slope of thistle
and buttercup, spread bark to keep down weeds clearing
a little more summer garden from the jungle.

LIANE ELLISON NORMAN

The Weeping of Trees

Haggard after what she said was a sleepless night,
Miss Boyd, Professor of Medieval Literature,
neat plaid wool jumper, gray hair escaping
from hairpins, opals on eight fingers where
only those born in October could wear them.
The trees, cut down that day had cried aloud

all night, kept her from sleeping. In our backyard,
squirrels run up to the sliced-off stump
of the century-old maple stop short, unwilling
to walk on the raw sliced trunk, 12 feet around,
the world they've known, vanished from among
the trampled ferns, hostas, the fresh sawdust.

The Making of the Dark Knight

He said: "We're early."

"Traffic wasn't bad," she said, shifting her purse from one shoulder to the other. Bright green with a huge plastic flower on one side, it was heavy, full of everything she might need and some things she would never need. "We made good time."

"I didn't notice the traffic."

"Of course you didn't notice. You were asleep."

"I was tired."

"Lucky we got a meter with time on it." She smiled at him.

"Yeah, right. Lucky. That's what we are. Lucky." He walked towards the intersection. They paused at the corner, waiting for the robotic white man to give permission to cross. The light changed, the white man lit up. They crossed the street with an assortment of others, a hunched over old woman in a bright pink shawl and frayed straw hat, a tall man in a gray suit with leather briefcase, teen girls with bare shoulders and flip-flops that slapped against their feet. Down the street she saw a large crane; its long neck like a great metal giraffe's stretched above the streetlights. Orange cones stood as street barriers near police cars, lights flashing.

She nudged his arm; he pulled away. "Look down there. They're getting ready to film *The Dark Knight*." The band of his watch was loose; he slid it on his wrist to see the time. She frowned. "You didn't even look." He shrugged. "Let's go see the movie when it comes out. Watch for people we know who are extras." She watched his face, waiting for his reaction.

He only said again: "We're early."

"I know. Maybe we could get some breakfast. We have time."

"I'm not hungry."

"All right then. Maybe just coffee?" She motioned to a woman nearby. "Excuse me," she said. The woman was craning her neck towards the filming. "Excuse me," she said again, louder. "Can you tell me a good place for breakfast or coffee? Some place nearby?"

The woman smiled. "Pamela's. Right there on the other side of Forbes, a block down. You know the *Pres-i-dent* ate there." She pointed; her fingernails were long, painted a brilliant red. "Cross back over the intersection and make a left. Then cross at Atwood."

"Thanks. Sounds like just the place."

"So we're crossing another intersection?"

"Yes. At least one."

Pamela's was low and squat, dwarfed by sprawling hospitals, ancient churches. The Cathedral of Learning towered in the background. Inside, people clustered by the door, waiting. It was narrow and long like a railroad dining car that had jumped its track and was stuck there in Oakland. Small tables ran along each side. Waiters turned sideways to pass each other in the center aisle. Back-to-back, butt-to-butt they passed, carrying plates of pancakes and eggs. A hand-lettered note taped to the cash register read: "Sorry, no debit or credit cards. $$ Cash only $$." She pulled her wallet out of her purse—a twenty, a ten and some crumpled ones, folded upon each other.

Once they were seated, she opened her menu, a tri-fold piece of blue paper with a blood-red smear of ketchup along its edge. He laid his menu down, unopened. "Anything to drink?" the waitress asked and smiled. There was a gap between her front teeth.

"Coffee, no cream, and water, please."

"And for you, sir?

"Nothing." She walked to the counter, "Banana Walnut Hotcakes" printed in large letters across the back of her tee shirt, the words stacked one on top of the other like hotcakes.

The coffee was hot and pungent with the smell of newly roasted coffee beans. Steam swirled up in a light mist. She sat the coffee aside to let it cool. "Ready to order?" The waitress took a pencil from behind her ear and an order pad from her back pocket.

"I'll have the spinach feta omelet. It sounds healthy. Don't you think it sounds healthy?"

The waitress nodded. "And for you?" She looked at the husband.

"Nothing."

"Nothing? Do you want two plates so you can share?"

"No. I want nothing."

They sat in silence. Around them, people talked, laughed, ate. When the waitress brought the omelet, so large the edges draped over the plate rim, she asked, "Is it true the President ate here?"

"Wish it was. I'da loved waiting on him. He ate at the other Pamela's, down in the Strip." She laid the bill face down between them. "You know he flew the owners, Pam and Gail, to the White House for some special breakfast? Just imagine. Wish he'd eaten here. More coffee?"

The woman shook her head. The waitress moved to the next table.

"Imagine," the woman said. "The President might have eaten here. If he hadn't gone to the Strip. Might have sat at this very table."

"It's not important. 'Might have' is not important. So stop talking." She couldn't finish her omelet. It was either too big or she was no longer hungry. "How far away is the office?" he asked.

"Couple of blocks. The Falk building, corner of Fifth and Lothrop."

"That's uphill from here?" He looked at his watch again, sliding it again to see the face.

"It's Pittsburgh. Everything is either uphill or downhill. You know that." He looked away as she picked up the bill. She took her wallet out of her purse and checked for her little green notebook and pen in the side pouch. "Look," she said, holding up the notebook. "I'm going to take notes."

"You think I won't remember what he says?"

"I thought it would be a good idea. You know. To take notes."

"Stop talking." They walked in silence uphill.

And it's 1984 David Bowie

in *Labyrinth*, the blonde hair
straight in glittered glory.

And I am Sarah, dark hair,
eyes fixed with David's stars,

moonlight in the sparkle of me.
But in my version David can take

me, I'll be the love slave to the white-blue
shadows of his eyes. He can turn the stupid

blonde baby into a goblin, keep baby/household
chores/the domestic demands of stepmother.

Take me deep into the unreal, the stairs
leading to nowhere, the great fall; take

me into the black thickness of 80s hair.
Then I will know I belong to Bowie's

Underground, my goblin king/no need
for teasing with the dark of my natural head.

The same shit she always does

I am thinkin of my fav sista! Miss you Rina!
Wish you were here!
Devanne facebooks on my wall, spiraling
letters pushing out on the blinking laptop screen.
But what I think of is money drained
from our mother, me sending checks/almost
stopping payment at the last second.
Devanne's *oh you bought me…this.*
About my non-name brand Christmas gifts—
her trashing my journals, stealing my bras,
locking me out of my bedroom. I think of her
room perfectly intact back home, mine now an office.
The burns and calluses on my working hands…
her hands smooth and unblemished from never
waiting tables. Right now, she's sitting at some table in
Lisbon, Portugal, sipping a cappuccino paid for by
our father's credit card, blogging and wishing I was
there to maybe pay for her extra slice of pie.

DORINA PENA

When the Mask Slips

We wear the mask that grins and lies,
It hides our cheeks and shades our eyes—
This debt we pay to human guile;
With torn and bleeding hearts we smile.
—*We Wear the Mask*, Paul Laurence Dunbar

What hell is revealed when the mask slips? Red bursts of blood soaked rivers flow like volcanic lava burning you alive. So hot the devil screams to Heaven for mercy and his pleas to be saved are ignored.

"Do you think you need to see a counselor about your anger issue?" My office manager, looked smug, like she had boxed me in to a corner.

Bitch, I will jump over this table and slap the fucking shit out your mouth, I thought to myself. My fingers gripped the bottom of the fabric-covered office chair as the sensation of a bolt of white lightning filled my eyes, blinding me for a brief moment. My lips fought with my tongue to think before speaking. I wanted to do battle. It felt as though all the years of rage I had successfully buried deeply inside would burst like the Ninth Ward levees during Hurricane Katrina and it would drain my consciousness of every decent belief I had about most white people, especially those in a position of power over others. Then I would become that mythical bitter, angry black woman, the feared Black Bitch.

The tightness in my chest was unbearable. I wanted to pierce the pain with a knife and release that thing inside me. That monster fed by years of being subjected to racist attitudes has evolved. This simmering monster, who wants to break out and burn everything in sight, with black fist raised high and voices screaming burn baby, burn. The rage of blackness is red, like the flames of city streets when Martin Luther King was assassinated. This is my anger.

On a beautiful summer day, 1974, a group of my girlfriends and I were driving through a small quiet town in Beaver County (Pennsylvania) hanging out and having fun. Suddenly a shiny color pickup truck sped up from behind our car and two white boys yelled out the window and called us niggers and then sped off.

What is it with white boys in pickup trucks? What is it with white boys screaming the word nigger, but never staying around long enough to face the consequences? Their words and anger festered in me and returned again and again from many a fair face.

Walking home with my friends, the breeze felt like lukewarm bathwater and the orange fall leaves swirled gently around my feet. In Sewickley, the small town I grew up in, each fall brought the Harvest Festival with its games, rides and carnival foods. Anticipation of the coming festival occupied our conversations as we walked.

'Hey, Pete. I'm going to kick your ass,' a voice screamed from the darkened house on the corner. That was where Greg Ryder lived. Their house was large enough for his five brothers and his dad who was a borough policeman.

'Do you hear me?' He screamed again. We couldn't see him clearly as their yard was filled with discarded car engine parts, wood planks and an abandoned above ground swimming pool. Their large makeshift garage with its' mismatched windows was filled with cars and motorcycles in various stages of disrepair. Not to mention the tires strewn the entire driveway. He could have been hiding anywhere in the yard.

'He's crazy,' Anthony, my boyfriend at the time, said as he looked at me and squeezed my hand.

'Yeah, he's must think you're Pete. I mean both of you are tall. It's dark. He can't tell the difference.' I answered.

The pace of our little group quickened.

'You hear me Pete. I'm coming to get you,' Greg screamed again.

'Tell him, you're not Pete. He's crazy,' I urged my boyfriend.

'Pete's not with us,' he screamed as we continued to walk fast in the opposite direction.

　　　　　　　　　　　　　　　　BONITA LEE PENN

'Shut the fuck-up. You lying nigger,' Greg screamed back. Just then the sound of a muffler-less truck started up. It sounded as though it had jumped the curb and the frame was shaking so badly it might fall apart before it reached us. Suddenly screams came from the group as the tank-looking truck caught up to us.

'Pete is not with us. What's your problem?' my boyfriend screamed at the figure in the driver's side. By this time I knew we were close to the corner as the scent of the homemade wine was strong. In the background we could hear the opening of screen doors and a jumble of voices speaking Italian. We had reached the block where most of the Italian families in Sewickley lived.

'Fucking nigger. You're not going to mess with me again,' Greg screamed and then the booming sound of a gunshot filled the night air.

I felt my boyfriend grab my arm and pull me in the direction of my house a couple of blocks away. Others in the group broke off and ran down Nevin Avenue to the safety of their own homes, some hid behind cars, and a few quickly jumped behind the bushes lining the yards.

'I'm going to call the police,' a voice in broken English screamed. I heard the rattling of the truck in the distance, going in the opposite direction.

Rattle

She turns out the light and flops into bed, exhausted. A sound migrates across the room from the open window. A scratching or scraping, but not exactly. It seems to be coming from below, maybe outside the kitchen window. Did she leave it unlocked? Wide open? It had been Ethan's job to check the windows before bed. What if someone is slicing the screen with a knife? She squeezes her eyes shut, pulls the sheet over her head. She wants her phone, but it's on the dresser, charging. Why is she frozen like a scared rabbit instead of dashing away with the speed of a gazelle chased by a lion?

She couldn't scream if she had to, like those many Christmases ago when she tiptoed down the stairs believing she heard Santa, and several steps from the bottom, came eye-to-eye with a mean-faced man without a beard or a Santa hat. He carried two trash bags with pointy bulges; nothing lay under the tree. The doll she asked for, the one that cried real tears, wouldn't be able to breathe if it was in the bag. As she watched the man leave, she couldn't breathe, like she can't breathe now. So tense, it hurts. If only Ethan were next to her. Not even a lock on the bedroom door to protect her. Sweat soaks her nightshirt and makes her feel almost as drenched as she was this morning.

She was terrified then, too, when she tipped the canoe on her first outing alone since Ethan left. She'd kept their reservation with the boat outfitters and enjoyed the day, hadn't she? Except for the dunk. Her ears still hold the water. It's only the river water trying to escape that she hears; yeah, that's all, no burglar. So why can't she relax?

This tightness, this lack of air, she hates it as much as she hates that Ethan left. Hates all these feelings so much she would run from them if she could, like the time she refused to eat the stinking liver—strange to remember this now. Her mother pried her mouth open to force it in, and when it touched her tongue, she tumbled off the chair, scrambled out the kitchen door and

KATHRYN KATAFIASZ PEPPER

hid in the shrubbery, too scared to answer her mother's calls, and fell asleep in the dark. But she can't hide now, can't sleep now, didn't sleep last night or the night before or the one before that, thinking about how Ethan walked out and there was nothing she could do to stop him.

She's so tired, she has to sleep, has to talk herself down from this fear—okay, it's quiet now. Maybe the wind scraped a branch against the house. Ethan would know what to say if he were here where he belongs, the bastard.

What was that clunk? What if someone really is breaking in? Her stomach roils like a flooding river. He'll have a knife or a gun and creep up the stairs into the bedroom and—

There's not enough air in here; she could suffocate. She almost suffocated this morning when she swam towards the river bottom instead of up, pain searing her lungs. Panic kept her from seeking the light until she forced herself to open her eyes in the muck to find the way up.

She needs to open her eyes now, get the phone, find out what's there. She can do it. She pulls the sheet off her head and slides it down her arms, smells the damp night air, sees shadows of branches on the wall, feels her feet sink into the rug, winces at the almost-physical pain in her heart, folds herself into a crouch to scuttle to the window, peers out to see a raccoon climbing on fallen trash cans.

Oh. She's all worked up over a raccoon. Just a hungry raccoon. No reason to fear dying, facing that nothingness alone. At least not tonight. So why is she still frightened? Life as she knew it died when Ethan left. What will she do without him? Hot tears erupt. Hands in fists, she pounds on the window frame to scare off the raccoon. The glass rattles. Making a life without Ethan—that's what really scares her. The raccoon lumbers away, but she keeps on pounding and pounding.

My Father Dreamed of Building Bridges

Worked with his father, a stone mason contractor
in a city of bridges—the Smithfield Street Bridge
inspired his steel truss student design—
knew metals, how steel contracts and expands,
master of the slide rule. For forty years calculated
construction costs for mills and plants, but bridges—
only in highway projects. Hanging onto his dream

into retirement, found a protégé, a PennDOT Engineer,
his youngest niece. Their talk only engineers could
comprehend. She fathomed his fascination with bridges:
Your dad was a structures kind of guy;
the ultimate for a civil engineer—bridge design—
a span grounded shore to shore arching skyward.
It's the aesthetic.

On our last driving trip, Dad drove, cautiously, navigating
on secondary roads in his Ford Taurus, familiar routes,
on roads that he drove with his mother in a used Model T,
on roads that bridged streams, valleys and railroad tracks
to Wheeling, West Virginia. He crossed and
recrossed that soaring suspension bridge
over the Ohio River.

ANNE PICONE

Before Sleep, I Think of Darwin

At the dinner party, Darwin says to Noah:
"What about the pterodactyl?"
Noah says, "Just ran out of time."
A green light pulses in the mirror,
the CO monitor. After 200 pulses I stop
counting. Now Darwin has *me* thinking:
I can't remember how to do cube roots.
I hold the image of a candle flame,
meditate on emptiness—*Inhale, relax,*
exhale, relax. No coffee, no tea,
but still the Darwin influence:
can anti-matter be another term for dark matter?
I throw off covers, stumble to the living room.
Lights on, Rebecca West's *Black Lamb*
and Grey Falcon offers Yugoslavia.
Bookmarked p. 269.

Desert, Speaking

When the voice in the burning creosote
peeled his mind, he knew he'd entered
a *no passing zone*, walking the dead-end
desert, intrigued by yellow dust that swirled
around his ankles. Before him rose
a toll booth basket he thought to fill
with worthiness he couldn't find inside,
the image of his Chevy powered
by a cosmic wind. His mind shimmied
as he found himself before a sign that read,
No exit. He needed no cop car siren to hear
the voice. After trying out "I've got a lot
to do," "I have to meet a man," "It's my
girlfriend's birthday," he heard his voice
say "Yes," his mind emptied of himself.

SUSAN SHAW SAILER

backwards and forwards

after a thief creeps
unbidden, a water straw is a good defense—
blow bubbles invisible in the cool wet air.

a little leaf falls
unnoticed in a new fen,
then dance.

lemon novice / novice lemon
but there is an error of order

rearrange the crumpled paper trap,
blow it away to wrap shilling fish.

the worry that creeps may be enticed
yet, stop fist / twirl / dance
in cool citrus breeze.

Horizontal Ground Target

Grams & Aunt Mart spent hours
sitting at the picnic table in Aunt Mart's yard.
In summer, they ate cantaloupe halves filled with vanilla ice cream;
wouldn't allow us to play with the lawn darts,
were convinced we would each lose at least one eye.

Somewhere Between Pittsburgh and Cleveland

Half asleep,
in the front seat of your car,
listening to Hendrix
I think about:

how we just bought thirteen bottles of Pink Grapefruit hand soap,
figured it would last about six years, and

how, when the interstate was snow-covered,
you said: *If we start to crash*
  don't tense up.

Return Visit

She calls it an abomination, to utter these words:

grow old gracefully? as she runs wrinkled fingers

across her aging face, massages loose flesh under

her chin.

I see Mother often these days, she stands at my mirror,

hairbrush in hand, coaxing gray strands to move,

cover bald spaces in the crown of her head.

It's ironic how past becomes presence,

present becomes past, no matter the length of time,

Mother lives on.

SHIRLEY SNODEY

The Rock Corner Ladies

Twelve years old, naïve and impressionable

intrigued by the ladies who lived in

the red brick house on Rock Corner Way.

She watched them lean over splintered wooden banisters,

their bosoms revealed in peek-a-boo blouses, their

pompadour hairdos and ox-blood lipstick.

Some men passed them by, others ascended the porch steps

on Saturday nights with pay-check money.

Her mind left dowdy mothers, bellies heavy with child,

that stood barefoot frying chicken in hot kitchens

on potbelly stoves.

This Is Your Brain on Fruit

after Robin Behn

Brain says: Smell this.
Brain says: orange or apricot?

Juicy, almost too sweet
licking the pit, flavor.

Locally grown and I don't
want to wash off the skin.
Taste   the dirt, the insect poop
the picker's hands plucking it
caressing it   smoothing it
all over.

Brains asks: When was the last time
          you got laid?

Laid   screwed   banged   do me   do me
doomedoobiedoobie doo wop!

My mother said only sluts lose it
in the backseats of cars.

Sluts   Mutts   Putz
putzing around the produce section
for something different?   exotic?   Fresh?

brain says: just get some
               iceberg and
                    cherry tomatoes.

BERNADETTE ULSAMER

This Unclean Spring

Wet snowfall in March—robins on a head trip:

shrub, to branch

      to power wires

—*PEEK!! tut tut tut tut*—

picking up bits of coarse grass, twigs, paper.

—*seeech each-each-each*—

More grey than reddish-orange breasts
      (last summer's freckles on my chest)

Spots of green sprouted early despite the cold,

shudder in the wet wind.
      (this unclean spring)—

Even with winter boots standing ready by the front door,

I use the weather as an excuse to avoid people.

These first robins dredge

half frozen ground, search for

beetle grubs and caterpillar,
      smeared mud.

Dancer at the American Legion

Mike books partners 3 weeks in advance,
dances 12 sets with different ladies,
each week.
Like Fred Rogers, he wears sweaters
lots of blue, some yellow
pants, no tie,
dresses his face with a smile, sewn tight.

It is Mike's smile you first notice,
flourishes from inside a body
so thin and frail,
bent over like some wind is pushing him.

I watch him smile at the table
where we talk,
I watch his smile when he dances the swing,
tango, fox trot.
It is an all-night look that makes me wonder
if it's hard to do—
makes me wonder if he takes it home.

Mike's eyes capture your face
like a camera designed to remember you.
He talks about dinners he cooks with his son,
asks about you.

Last week Mike handed me a cassette of songs,
smiled, told me to find the selections he likes best.
I said, *How would I know?*
I listened long hours to 20 versions of the Argentina tango.

ANN UNGAR

The Five Black Piano Keys

inspired by gospel singer Wintley Phipps' history of "Amazing Grace"

It's *The West African Sorrow Chant*
heard from the belly of the slave ship,
in *pentatonic scale*, the haunted hums
of groans from pains, fears and cries
of grief, wailed into the night, known
as the *slave scale* by the Captain and
mates on the ship.

The sounds grow louder in rough seas,
terror of the big waters, the sinking ship,
the lashings, the chains, the White Devils.
Will they eat us?

The slaves prayed to their ancestral spirits,
practiced indigenous religions,
destinations unknown, so in unison
shouted to the Voodoo Gods, *save us*.

Chants were in many tongues, begging for
compassion, their animated spirits, absorbed in a
melodic composed rhythm, articulated in sounds of
The Black Piano Keys.

the retiree

another day
but no more dollars
for him who's retired

decrepit—he sits on
a chair that he built
from a mail-order kit

wearing old jeans
he two fingers
on typewriter keys

googles for tunes
tweets buddies
surfs the wide web for

news of the world
as seen on an H/P
computer screen

LUCIENNE WALD

Sisters

My father's two sisters,
Louise and Lovara,
both widowed,
were neighbors.
If they happened
to meet, they nodded
but never spoke.

My mother, Rose,
and her sister, Marguerite,
quarreled before being
separated by the Atlantic.
They didn't correspond
until the day my mother
received a letter from France.
Her sister wrote, "I'm dying.
Let's make up. I forgive you
for hating me all these years."

Mother answered, "Whatever
makes you think I hated you?
It was you who had a grievance
of some kind against me."

My sister and I live far apart
we seldom meet
but when we do
we are far from speechless.
We disagree a lot
as did our parents,
but not so loud.

LUCIENNE WALD

The Stone of Me

you lay your arm around me
I feel its weight

we sleep

I wake

to find your arm
but not weight

does sleep erase weight

help us float

water lifting in dream—if

this is what it means
to be your lover

I agree

weightless your arm holds

the stone of me

GAIL LANGSTROTH
2011 PATRICIA DOBLER POETRY AWARD WINNER

About the 2011 Patricia Dobler Poetry Award Winner

GAIL LANGSTROTH was born in Ardmore, Oklahoma, and spent her youth in Montana. After receiving her BA degree in liberal arts from Connecticut College (1972) and her diploma as a performer and teacher of Eurythmy from Else Klink, Das Eurythmeum, Stuttgart, Germany (1976), she became a member of the Stuttgart Stage Group, performing worldwide for the following eight years. In 1984, she moved to Santander, Spain, where her concentration on the guitar and the Spanish language inspired her further expression as both poet and performer. Collaborating with international artists in North and South America, Japan, Spain, Germany, Russia, and Romania, she has created and performed numerous productions, including *Dawn*, a performance based on the Book of Revelation, *Light Cracks*, *Aripa frinta*, *El Camino*, *Elegiacs I and II*, *Siegelworte*, and *Opus 131*. In June of 2011 she received her MFA in poetry at Drew University, Madison, N.J.

About the 2011 Patricia Dobler Poetry Award Judge

DENISE DUHAMEL was born in Woonsocket, Rhode Island. She received a BFA degree from Emerson College and an MFA degree from Sarah Lawrence College. She is the author of numerous books and chapbooks of poetry, most recently *Ka-Ching!* (University of Pittsburgh, 2009), *Two and Two* (2005), and *Mille et un sentiments* (Firewheel Editions, 2005). Her other books currently in print are *Queen for a Day: Selected and New Poems* (University of Pittsburgh, 2001); *The Star-Spangled Banner*, winner of the Crab Orchard Poetry Prize (1999); *Kinky* (1997); *Girl Soldier* (1996); and *How the Sky Fell* (1996). Duhamel has also collaborated with Maureen Seaton on three volumes: *Little Novels* (Pearl Editions, 2002), *Oyl* (2000), and *Exquisite Politics* (Tia Chucha Press, 1997). A winner of a National Endowment for the Arts Fellowship, she has been anthologized widely, including four volumes of *The Best American Poetry* (2000, 1998, 1994, and 1993). Duhamel teaches creative writing and literature at Florida International University and lives in Hollywood, Florida.

At the Brera, Milan

The breadth of the chest
seems immense, the face strained as if
in troubled sleep, the marble stillness of the corpse
matches the red-veined marble table
on which the body rests.
There is no place else to look, we are thrust
almost atop the body. Its torn flesh,
from which no blood flows, is draped with linen.
Foreshortened legs and tiny feet. Look,
there is a jar of ointment by the pillowed head.
Beyond, an open door leading to a burial room.
The body seems beyond decay with its flowing hair,
smooth, bent arms, and hands loosely curled
into cloth as liquid and still as poured stone.
At the center of the canvas, the bulging drapery
at the loins reminds us this had been a man in his vigor
now stretched on a slab as if poised
to catapult into our midst.
The world to come has not entered here.
A reddish glow covers everything, and even
the weeping figures shunted to the side—
St. John, the Virgin, Mary Magdalene—
aged, ravaged with grief, are incidental
to this *Dead Christ* Mantegna
painted for his own funerary chapel
which stands before us as if made
for our own, the room of our witness,
which we enter, and are still.

About the 2012 Patricia Dobler Poetry Award Winner

MICHELLE MAHER is a professor of English at La Roche College, a private, Catholic college north of Pittsburgh. She has two Master's degrees and a PhD in English from Indiana University, Bloomington. Her poems have appeared most recently in *The Georgetown Review*, *The Atlantic Review*, *Pittsburgh City Paper*, *U.S. 1 Worksheets*, and *Voices from the Attic*.

About the 2012 Patricia Dobler Poetry Award Judge

TOI DERRICOTTE is the author of five books of poetry, the latest of which is *The Undertaker's Daughter* (University of Pittsburgh Press, 2011), hailed by Terrance Hayes as "her most stirring and innovative work yet." Her other volumes are *Tender*, winner of the 1998 Paterson Poetry Prize; *Captivity*; *Natural Birth*; and *The Empress of the Death House*. Of her poems, Audre Lorde wrote, "Because the power of her images breeds visions which are neither easy nor inescapable, Toi Derricotte moves us.... The pain does not exceed the power." Derricotte's literary memoir, *The Black Notebooks*, won the 1998 Anisfield-Wolf Book Award for Nonfiction and was a *New York Times* Notable Book of the Year. Her essay "Beginning Dialogues" is included in *The Best American Essays 2006*, edited by Lauren Slater. Additional honors include the Lucille Medwick Memorial Award from the Poetry Society of America; two Pushcart Prizes; the Distinguished Pioneering of the Arts Award from the United Black Artists; the New York Graduate School of Arts & Science Alumni Achievement Award; the Barnes & Noble Writers for Writers Award from Poets & Writers, Inc.; the Elizabeth Kray Award for service to the field of poetry from Poets House; and fellowships from the National Endowment for the Arts, the Rockefeller Foundation, and the Guggenheim Foundation. With Cornelius Eady, in 1996, she co-founded Cave Canem Foundation, North America's premier "home for black poetry." She is a professor of English at the University of Pittsburgh and serves on the Academy of American Poets' Board of Chancellors.

About the Patricia Dobler Poetry Award

This contest is open to women writers over the age of 40 who are United States citizens or permanent residents, currently living in the United States, who have not published a full-length book of poetry, fiction, or nonfiction (chapbooks excluded). Current Carlow students or employees are not eligible.

The winner receives the Patricia Dobler Poetry Award, valued at $2,500, in the form of round-trip travel and lodging as a participating guest of Carlow's MFA residency in Pittsburgh, PA; publication in *Voices from the Attic*; and a reading at Carlow University in Pittsburgh with the final judge.

Poems must be unpublished, up to 75 lines or fewer per poem; up to two poems, of any style, per submission.

All entrants receive a copy of *Voices from the Attic*.

For information on the Patricia Dobler Poetry Award, or Carlow University's MFA program, please visit www.carlow.edu or contact Ellie Wymard, PhD, at 412.578.6346.

Notes

"Sunset Turns," by Judith A. Brice, page 25, will be published in *Renditions in a Palette*, © 2013. Reprinted by permission of Wordtech Communications.

"The world is a beautiful place," by Doralee Brooks, page 27, is after Lawrence Ferlinghetti's "The World Is a Beautiful Place."

The first line of "From the Canal," by Angele Ellis, page 56, is from Anne Marie Rooney's "Last Evening: Index of First Lines."

"hydrangea and free fall" and "Some days I am," by Lois I. Greenberg, pages 68-69, were originally published in *Willing to Lie*, © 2012. Reprinted by permission of MadBooks.

"Dear Hysteria," by Jill Khoury, page 79, uses lyrics from David Bowie's "Rebel Rebel."

"This Is Your Brain on Fruit," by Bernadette Ulsamer, page 107, is after the poet Robin Behn.

"The Five Black Piano Keys," by Beatrice W. Vasser, page 110, is inspired by gospel singer Wintley Phipps' history of "Amazing Grace."

About the Madwomen

LISA ALEXANDER earned a BA in creative writing from Carlow University in 2010, and is working towards an MFA at Drew University. Her work has been published in *The Carlow Journal*, *The Palimpsest Review*, *Girls with Glasses*, and *Burnside Review*, and is forthcoming in *Bloom*. She is a sound engineer for *Prosody*, NPR-affiliate WYEP's weekly radio show featuring poets and writers.

MADALON AMENTA is the author of *Kandinsky and the Stars*, a chapbook published in 2010 by Finishing Line Press. A seven-year member of the Madwomen in the Attic, her poetry has appeared in *Salon.com*, *Pittsburgh City Paper*, *Pittsburgh Post-Gazette*, *Signatures*, and *Stories about Time*. She has also published over 80 clinical and academic papers, manuals, newsletters, research reports, and books, one of which won an *American Journal of Nursing* Book of the Year Award.

LAURIE ARNOLD is a nurse whose passion is therapeutic writing and facilitating the group process using poetry as inspiration for writing and healing. She especially loves poetry for its concise power and ability to move people so readily and to think in new ways.

EILEEN ARTHURS holds a BA from George Washington University and an MFA from Carlow University. Her novel, *Lorelei's Family*, is available for Kindle and Nook. She won an honorable mention in Writelink's winter competition for her short story *Christmas Spirits*. Her short story collection, *Stories in the Key of XX*, is forthcoming. She also is working on a novel-in-progress, *Sweetie-pie*.

MADELEINE BARNES is a student at Carnegie Mellon University, majoring in creative writing and fine arts. Her poems have appeared in *The Rattling Wall, Pittsburgh Post-Gazette, 5AM, Allegheny Review, Plain China, North Central Review*, and *The Albion Review*. In 2011, she won the Women's Press Club of Pittsburgh's Gertrude Gordon Writing Contest, funded by The Pittsburgh Foundation. She placed first in the Princeton Poetry Prize and the Borders Open Door Poetry Contest judged by Billy Collins, who is featured reading her poem on the Borders website.

TESS BARRY has an MA in English from the University of Pittsburgh and is enrolled in Carlow University's MFA program. Her work has appeared most recently in *Natural Language: Carnegie Library of Pittsburgh Sunday Poetry and Reading Series Anthology, Girls with Glasses*, and *Sampsonia Way*, an online magazine sponsored by City of Asylum/Pittsburgh. She has been a guest poet on WYEP's weekly radio show, *Prosody*.

JOAN E. BAUER's full-length book of poetry, *The Almost Sound of Drowning*, was published by Main Street Rag in 2008. Her poems have appeared in *5AM, The New Renaissance, Poet Lore, Quarterly West*, and *Slipstream*. Her work has also appeared in various anthologies, including *Along These Rivers: Poetry and Photography from Pittsburgh* (Quadrant, 2008), *Come Together: Imagine Peace* (Bottom Dog Press, 2008) and *Only the Sea Keeps: Poetry of the Tsunami* (Bayeux Arts, 2005), which she co-edited with Judith Robinson and Sankar Roy. With Jimmy Cvetic, she organizes and co-hosts the Hemingway's Summer Reading Series in Pittsburgh.

JOAN HUBER BERARDINELLI is a retired English professor who developed and coordinated writing centers at Davis & Elkins College (West Virginia) and the Venango Campus of Clarion University. Currently, she works on resumes, edits, and tutors.

KAREN KORNBLUM BERNTSEN holds a BFA from the University of Michigan and a Master of Science in interactive media from Duquesne University. While at Michigan, she received the Hopwood Award for poetry. In Chicago, she opened her own company, Forté Design, in 1989. She has received numerous national and international awards for her design work, and her work was included in the opening of the Museum of Contemporary Art in Chicago, and a major exhibit and book for the Carnegie Museum of Art. She has taught courses in design at Carnegie Mellon University, where she served on the faculty for six years. She started writing poetry again, in 2008, after a long pause of thirty years.

GERRY ROSELLA BOCCELLA is an educator, designer, and arts advocate. She graduated from Carlow University (then Mount Mercy) in 1958. In 1994, she received the Carlow Alumnae Service Award in the Arts, followed in 1996 by the Carlow Woman of Spirit® Award for her work in the arts with at-risk youth. Her poetry has been featured on the WYEP-FM radio show, *Prosody*, and in the *Pittsburgh Post-Gazette* and *Pittsburgh City Paper*.

DORIT BRAUER is an artist, writer, poet, and the owner of the successful holistic medicine business Live Your Best Life. Her artistic resume includes solo art shows in Tel Aviv, Jerusalem, and En Hod in Israel; Bonn, Kalkar, and Krefeld in Germany, and Pittsburgh, Pennsylvania, as well as participation in group exhibits in Israel, Germany, and the United States. She is the author of the upcoming book, *Girls Don't Ride Motorbikes–A Spiritual Adventure Into Life's Labyrinth*, chronicling her modern day pilgrimage, a 7,430 mile solo motorcycle adventure across the United States to walk labyrinths.

JUDITH A. BRICE is the author of *Renditions in a Palette*, to be published by Wordtech Communications in 2013. She has had work published in the *Pittsburgh Post-Gazette*, *Pittsburgh City Paper*, *Paterson Literary Review*, *Poesia*, and *The Lyric*. She has received the Editor's Choice Award in the Alan Ginsberg

Poetry Contest in the 2008 *Paterson Literary Review* for one of her poems, and another poem is currently in the permanent archives of the Holocaust Memorial Center in Farmington Hills, Michigan.

DORALEE BROOKS is a Cave Canem fellow, and a teacher-consultant with the Western Pennsylvania Writing Project. She teaches in the Developmental Studies Department at the Community College of Allegheny County. Her poems have appeared in the *Pennsylvania Literary Journal, Pittsburgh Post-Gazette*, and *Callaloo*.

DANIELA BUCCILLI earned an MFA in fiction from the University of Pittsburgh in 2001. She is a fellow of the Western Pennsylvania Writing Project. Her poems have appeared in *The Fourth River, Pittsburgh Post-Gazette, Waterways: Poetry in the Mainstream, Dionne's Story, Pittsburgh City Paper, TheNewYinzer. com*, and *SubtleTea.com*. She has taught high school English since 1994.

JENNIFER BURNAU teaches in the Pittsburgh Public Schools, and is certified in English, music, and art. She has studied fiction with Evelyn Pierce and poetry with Stacey Waite.

KAIT BURRIER is a student in the Wilkes University Creative Writing MFA program with an emphasis on poetry and drama. She is a member of the Dramatists Guild and the Association of Writers and Writing Programs. She graduated from Duquesne University with a BA in theater arts and French.

GAYLE REED CARROLL's poems have appeared in *Innisfree Poetry Journal Online, Poet Lore, The Comstock Review, Pittsburgh City Paper*, and *Black River Review*. Wendell Berry chose her poem "Dementia" for the Merton Prize for Poetry of the Sacred, 2009. Her book manuscript, *Raking Leaves by Moonlight*, was a finalist for the 2010 Marick Press Poetry Prize.

Her chapbook manuscript, *Irretrievable Music*, was selected as a finalist in the Keystone Chapbook Prize 2009 from Seven Kitchens Press.

LAINY CARSLAW is currently working on a manuscript, *Just a Phase*. She is a graduate of the University of Pittsburgh's Writing Program. Her poem, "Winter to a Sculptor," was published in the 2000 edition of *The Writer's Review*.

SHEILA L. CARTER-JONES is the author of *Three Birds Deep*, selected by Elizabeth Alexander as the 2011 winner of the Naomi Long Madgett Poetry Book Award for African American writers (Lotus Press, Inc., 2012). She is also the author of a chapbook, *Blackberry Cobbler Song*. Her poetry is published in *Crossing Limits*, *Pittsburgh Quarterly*, *Tri-State Anthology*, *Riverspeak*, *Flights: The Literary Journal of Sinclair Community College*, and *Coal: A Poetry Anthology*. She is a Cave Canem fellow, and a fellow/teacher consultant for the Western Pennsylvania Writers Project at the University of Pittsburgh.

JOANIE CHAPPEL, a Pittsburgh native, moved to Los Angeles where she signed with 20th Century Fox as a songwriter/lyricist. Her songs have been recorded by Ronnie Milsap, Restless Heart, Chet Atkins, and Suzy Bogguss, among others. A portion of her novel-in-progress, *The Fireball*, was chosen as a finalist in the William Faulkner Creative Writing Competition. She is working on another novel, *A Room with Better Lighting*.

REBECCA COLE-TURNER is a spiritual director, retreat and pilgrimage leader, and dragon boater. Two of her poems were published in *HungryHearts*, a quarterly journal focused on spirituality, and several were published on the Mainline Protestant portal of Patheos.com on her blog, *Musings of a Meandering Pilgrim*. She is in the Masters of Divinity program at Pittsburgh Theological Seminary.

CJ COLEMAN teaches fifth and sixth grade creative writing at the Pittsburgh Gifted Center, and is a 2000 Western Pennsylvania Writing Project Fellow. Her poems have appeared in *Riverspeak*, *Threads*, and *Pittsburgh City Paper*.

KAY COMINI has been published in *Poet Lore*, *Pittsburgh City Paper*, *The Pittsburgh Quarterly*, and the anthologies *Dark Side of the Moon*, *Voices from the Parlor*, and in the Sandburg-Livesay anthology, *No Choice But to Trust*. Her chapbook, *The Picking Room*, placed second in the White Eagle Coffee Store Press 2010 Contest. She is a retired welfare caseworker, certified Gestalt therapist, and an energy healer.

ANN CURRAN is author of a chapbook, *Placement Test* (Main Street Rag). Her poetry has appeared in *Rosebud*, *U.S. 1 Worksheets*, *Blueline*, *Notre Dame Magazine*, *Ireland of the Welcomes*; and in the anthologies *Along These Rivers: Poetry and Photography from Pittsburgh*, *Motif 2 Come What May* (MotesBooks), and *Thatchwork* (Delaware Valley Poets, Inc.). She holds degrees from Duquesne University, where she also taught. She was a staff writer for the *Pittsburgh Post-Gazette* and *Pittsburgh Catholic*.

BARBARA DAHLBERG taught art in the Pittsburgh Public Schools for 11 years and Pace School for nine years. She is a 2001 Fellow of the Western Pennsylvania Writing Project and is a practicing artist.

VICTORIA DYM is a graduate of Ringling Brothers and Barnum & Bailey Clown College. She has earned an MFA in creative writing (poetry) from Carlow University and a BA in philosophy from the University of Pittsburgh. Dym's work has appeared in the *Pittsburgh Post-Gazette*, *Pittsburgh City Paper*, and *Pearl Magazine*. She is a certified Laughter Yoga Leader. She has taught poetry at the winter and summer Young Writer's Institutes, co-sponsored by the University of Pittsburgh and The Pittsburgh Cultural Trust.

ANGELE ELLIS is the author of two books of poems, *Spared* (Main Street Rag, 2011) and *Arab on Radar* (Six Gallery Press, 2007). Her work has been published in various journals, including *Issa's Untidy Hut, Girls with Glasses, Shine, Literazzi, Dionne's Story,* and *Make It So*. A 2008 recipient of an Individual Creative Artist Fellowship from the Pennsylvania Council on the Arts, she won Pittsburgh Filmmakers' G-20 Haiku Contest in 2009, and was a prizewinner in the 2007 RAWI Competition for Creative Prose. Her longtime peace and community activism led to co-authorship of the diversity workbook *Dealing With Differences* (Corwin Press, 1997).

CALEY FERGUSON graduated from West Virginia Wesleyan College in 2011 with a BA in English literature with minors in creative writing and gender studies. She is an Americorps member with Literacy*Americorps and teaches Adult Basic Education to members of the community through the education program at Goodwill of Southwestern Pennsylvania.

ALICE FUCHS has worked towards an MFA at the University of Pittsburgh. She has written four novels in a family saga series, and has published three poetry chapbooks: *Morning in Agrigento, Blood Poppies,* and *god L.* She lives on a farm in Washington County, Pa.

LAUREN GAULT is a junior creative nonfiction major at Carlow University. Her work has been published in *The Critical Point*. After graduation, she wishes to work for a Catholic publishing agency, and pursue publishing her creative writing.

NANCY GAYGAN is a poet and technical writer. She has been published in the *Pittsburgh Post-Gazette*, is the recipient of the Westmoreland Arts & Heritage Festival's poetry prize, and was a featured poet at the South Side Poetry Smorgasbord.

MARLENE GOLDSMITH is a clinical psychologist in private practice. She is also a published researcher and lecturer in

ABOUT THE MADWOMEN

the area of women and creativity. Her work has appeared in the *Pittsburgh Post-Gazette* and in an international anthology of poetry edited by the Serbian artist Todor Stevanović. She was awarded an honorable mention for one of her poems in the Tupelo Press Spring 2011 Poetry Project contest.

LOIS I. GREENBERG is the author of *Willing to Lie*, published in 2012 by MadBooks. Her poetry has appeared in *Paper Street, Pittsburgh Post-Gazette, HEArt (Human Equity Through Art), Pittsburgh City Paper*; in the anthologies *Electric Fire* (National Book Foundation), *Along These Rivers* (Quadrant), and *Alternatives To Surrender* (Martin Willetts, Jr. Ed.); in e-zines: hotmetalpress, paperstreetonline, and writersalliance; and on a *YAWP* CD. She was a finalist for the 2007 Patricia Dobler Poetry Award. She is a member of the Pittsburgh Poetry Exchange and the Advisory Board of Paper Street Press.

KAYE HARMON is working on a memoir which takes place in the mid-20th century. She has studied art history and photography at Chatham University. She has served as writer-editor for volunteer newsletters at Goodwill Industries and the Salvation Army Women's Auxiliary of Greater Pittsburgh, the latter of which she is a charter member and past president.

AMY LEE HEINLEN is pursuing an MFA degree in poetry from Chatham University, where she works as a librarian.

JANET INNAMORATO received a BA from the University of California at Los Angeles in 1977 and a JD from the University of Pittsburgh, School of Law.

CHRISTINA M. JELLISON is a senior poetry major at Carlow University. She is the Open Mic Emcee for The Hungry Sphinx Reading Series. Her work has been published in the 2008 edition of the *Ralph Munn Creative Writing Anthology*.

JILL KHOURY is the author of a chapbook, *Borrowed Bodies* (Pudding House, 2009). Her poems have appeared in numerous journals, including *Sentence*, *la fovea*, and *Harpur Palate*. She has been nominated for the Pushcart Prize twice by *Breath and Shadow: A Journal of Disability Culture and Literature*. Her most recent publications include a contribution to *Open Thread*, a regional review that features writers from Pennsylvania, Ohio, and West Virginia. She teaches writing and literature at Duquesne University.

MICHELLE MAHER is a professor of English at La Roche College in Pittsburgh, Pa. Her work has appeared or is forthcoming in *U.S. 1 Worksheets*, *Pittsburgh Post-Gazette*, *The Chautauqua Review*, *The Georgetown Review*, and *The Atlanta Review*.

EMILY MOHN helps run the first-year writing program at Carnegie Mellon University. She has published her poems in the *Pittsburgh Post-Gazette* and *Pittsburgh City Paper*, and has also taught middle-school English. She earned a BA from Colgate University, and an MA in English literature from Boston University.

MARILYN MARSH NOLL's chapbook, *Thirteen Ways of Looking at Bones*, won the Pennsylvania Poetry Society Chapbook Award in 2007. Her children's book, *Jonathan and the Flying Broomstick*, was published by Sunlight and Shadow Press in 2010. Her poems have appeared in the *Pittsburgh Post-Gazette*, *Folio*, and *Restonian*. Her poem, "Flaming Ice," is forthcoming in the *Comstock Review* in 2012. She received her MFA in creative writing at American University in Washington, D.C. in 1994.

LIANE ELLISON NORMAN is the author of two chapbooks: *Roundtrip*, published by Yesterday's Parties in 2012, and *Driving Near the Old Federal Arsenal*, published in

2011 by Finishing Line Press. Norman has also published two books of poetry, *The Duration of Grief* and *Keep*, a biography, a novel, and many articles, essays, and reviews. She has published poems in *The Fourth River, Hot Metal Press, 5AM, North American Review, Kestrel*, and the *Come Together: Imagine Peace* anthology. She won the Wisteria Prize in 2006 from Paper Journey Press.

HARRIET PARKE's work has been published in the *Pittsburgh Tribune-Review*, the *My Dad Is My Hero* anthology, and *Pittsburgh Magazine*. She won an honorable mention in *The Atlantic Monthly* student writing contest. She is completing final edits on a novel.

DORINA PENA is the author of *Leaving the Tree*, a chapbook published by MonkeyMan Press in 2011. She has been published in *Pittsburgh City Paper, Upstreet*, and *Girls with Glasses*. She received an MFA in creative writing (poetry) from Carlow University and a BA in English writing (poetry) from the University of Pittsburgh. Her full-length poetry manuscript is entitled *Masking White*.

BONITA LEE PENN is the author of *Visiting Rooms*, and a chapbook, *The B Side*. Her work has been published in *The Critical Point, Taj Mahal Review*, and *Crossing Limits: African Americans & American Jews: Poetry from Pittsburgh*. She is the managing-editor of the *Soul Pitt Quarterly*, and a freelance writer for Mentoring Showcase. She is pursuing a degree in creative writing at Carlow University.

KATHRYN KATAFIASZ PEPPER completed her MFA at Carlow University with the full-length novel, *Storm Dreams*. She also holds an MSEd from Duquesne University and certification in Life Coaching from Guiding Mindful Change. She teaches classes on compassionate self-discipline for writers called, *Write Now: The Other Side of Someday*.

ANNE PICONE's poem, "Duets," won a prize in the Ava Maria University Arts Festival Poetry Competition. A member of the Naples, Fla., Writer's Forum for four years, she is a retired English teacher with degrees from Duquesne University and the University of Pittsburgh.

SUSAN SHAW SAILER is the author of *Coal*, a chapbook published in 2011 by Finishing Line Press. Her poems have appeared in journals such as *5AM*, *Kestrel*, *Pearl*, and *Poetry International*. Her reviews and articles about poetry have appeared in *Indiana Review*, *Prairie Schooner*, and *Alehouse Review*. After retiring from the Department of English at West Virginia University, where she taught 20th Century Irish and British literature, Sailer completed an MFA in the Low-residency Program in Poetry at New England College in 2007.

TIFFANY A. TURBIN SANTOS' poetry, essays, and short stories have been published in several literary journals including *Backbone Mountain Review* and *Dionne's Story: An Anthology of Poetry and Prose for the Awareness of Relationship Violence*. She is pursuing an MFA in creative writing (poetry) from Carlow University. She graduated from St. Mary's College of Maryland with a self-designed BA in women, gender, and sexuality studies and a minor in Asian studies.

ERIKA SIMILO is a graduate of Bucknell University and the Duquesne University School of Law. Her poetry has appeared in *Pittsburgh City Paper* and the *Pittsburgh Post-Gazette*. She has been a guest poet on *Prosody*, WYEP's weekly radio show featuring poets and writers.

SHIRLEY SNODEY is the author of *Barefoot on Southern Soil*, a chapbook published in 2011 by MadBooks. She is a writer of poetry, fiction, and song lyrics, and is an eight-year member of the Madwomen in the Attic. She attended the Community

College of Allegheny County. Her poem, "Second Mourning," was published in *Pittsburgh City Paper*.

BERNADETTE ULSAMER earned a BA in poetry and an MLIS from University of Pittsburgh. She is pursuing her MFA in poetry at Carlow University. Her poetry has appeared in *Pittsburgh City Paper*, *The Main Street Rag*, and *Ophelia Street*, and been anthologized in *Along These Rivers: Poetry and Photography of Pittsburgh* and *Dionne's Story*. Ulsamer has also contributed and performed with the *Pittsburgh Monologue Project* and the *Hodge Podge Society*.

ANN UNGAR has published several poems in the *Minor Bird Literary Journal*. She earned her BA in English at Chatham University, where she received the Beatrice Lewis Memorial Award.

BEATRICE W. VASSER is the author of *Circle of Life: Verses From My Journey* (Pneuma Publishing, Inc., 2008). She is a retired teacher and licensed professional counselor. She earned her degrees from North Carolina Central University and received her PhD from the University of Pittsburgh. She has read in several venues in the Pittsburgh area, and attended workshops sponsored by Cave Canem and the Pittsburgh Center for the Arts.

LUCIENNE WALD has won awards in all three categories from the Westmoreland County Arts & Heritage Festivals. Her poetry has appeared in the *Pittsburgh Post-Gazette* and the *Leader Times*, an edition of the *Tribune-Review*. She is a native of St. Louis, Mo., and is bilingual in English and French. She has written one chapbook and is working on a second.

Madwomen History

The Madwomen in the Attic Writing Workshops, named after the groundbreaking study by Sandra Gilbert and Susan Gubar on the 19th-century woman writer, were founded in 1979 by Dr. Ellie Wymard, now director of the MFA program at Carlow, after a campus visit by the writer, Tillie Olsen. When Olsen was mobbed by women with stories, poems, and questions, it became clear that there was a hunger and a need for women's stories to be told. Over the years, visiting writers such as Tess Gallagher, Maggie Anderson, Alicia Ostriker, Marita Golden, Naomi Shihab Nye, Judith Vollmer, Maxine Kumin, Toi Derricotte, Denise Duhamel, and Jean Valentine would arrive to feed this hunger. The workshops were originally taught by Ellie Wymard. Esteemed fiction writer, Jane Candia Coleman, was the first director of the Madwomen, and later the beloved poet Patricia Dobler directed and developed the Madwomen in the Attic Workshops until her death in 2004. Patricia Dobler dedicated many years of her working life to the Madwomen to create an inclusive, vibrant atmosphere where women of varied backgrounds could meet and study the craft of writing. For this the Madwomen will be forever grateful.

About Patricia Dobler

Patricia Dobler was born in Middletown, Ohio, in 1939. She is the author of *UXB* (Mill Hunk Books, 1991) and *Talking to Strangers* (University of Wisconsin Press, 1986), which won the Brittingham Prize in Poetry; a chapbook, *Forget Your Life*, was published by the University of Nebraska Press. She also completed a third full-length collection, titled *Now*. Her poems have appeared in such publications as *Mid-American Review*, *The Ohio Review*, *Ploughshares*, *Prairie Schooner*, and *Southern Poetry Review*. Her work has been anthologized in *A Gathering of Poets*, *A New Geography of Poets*, *The Carnegie Mellon Anthology of Poetry*, *Working Classics*, *Vital Signs*, *Anthology of Magazine Verse & Yearbook of American Poetry*, and others. She has received grants from the National Endowment for the Arts, the Pennsylvania Council on the Arts, fellowships from the Corporation of Yaddo and Villa Montalvo, and a Pushcart Poetry prize. She lived in Pittsburgh, Pennsylvania, and taught for many years at Carlow University, where she directed the Women's Creative Writing Center, the Madwomen in the Attic Writing Workshops, and was instrumental in developing the MFA program. She died July 24, 2004. After her death, her *Collected Poems* was published by Autumn House Press in 2005.

The Editors

JAN BEATTY directs the Madwomen in the Attic writing workshops at Carlow University, where she is also director of creative writing and teaches in the low-residency MFA program. She is the author of three books of poetry, all published by the University of Pittsburgh Press: *Red Sugar*, finalist for the 2009 Paterson Poetry Prize; *Boneshaker*, finalist for the Milt Kessler Award; and *Mad River*, winner of the Agnes Lynch Starrett Prize. Her new chapbook, *Ravage*, was published by Lefty Blondie Press in 2012. Her newest book, *The Switching Yard*, is forthcoming from the University of Pittsburgh Press in 2013.

Beatty's limited edition chapbook, *Ravenous*, won the 1995 State Street Prize. Awards include the $15,000 Creative Achievement Award from the Pittsburgh Cultural Trust, the Pablo Neruda Prize for Poetry, and two fellowships from the Pennsylvania Council on the Arts. Her poetry has appeared in journals such as *Quarterly West*, *Gulf Coast*, *Indiana Review*, and *Court Green*; and in anthologies published by Oxford University Press, University of Illinois Press, and University of Iowa Press. For the past 18 years, she has hosted and produced *Prosody*, a public radio show on NPR-affiliate WYEP-FM, featuring the work of national writers.

NANCY KIRKWOOD teaches the Madwomen in the Attic nonfiction workshop. She holds a BA in creative writing from the University of Pittsburgh and an MFA in creative writing from Carlow University. She is an adjunct faculty member of Carlow University's English department and also works as an independent editor and writing coach. Her honors include the Schuylkill County Arts Fellowship Award, and publications in *Literary Mama*, *Pittsburgh City Paper*, and *Girls with Glasses*.

EVELYN PIERCE teaches the Madwomen in the Attic fiction workshop and undergraduate fiction at Carlow University. She has published short stories and two contracted screenplay adaptations, and is currently finishing her novel. She has been teaching writing since 1983, and is the recipient of multiple teaching honors. In 2004, she received the Sustained Excellence in Teaching Award at Carnegie Mellon University, where she teaches business management communication in the Tepper School of Business. She received her MFA in fiction from the University of Pittsburgh.

ELLEN MCGRATH SMITH teaches poetry for the Madwomen, as well as writing and literature at the University of Pittsburgh, where she earned an MFA in poetry in 1993. Her chapbook, *A Dog Makes His Rounds and Other Poems*, was published by Another Thing Press in 2002. Her poems have appeared in *5AM*, *The Prose Poem*, *Pearl*, *Southern Poetry Review*, *Chiron Review*, and *Kestrel*. Smith's awards include a recent honorable mention for the Lynda Hull Award from *Crazyhorse* and a 2007 Individual Artist Fellowship (Poetry) from the Pennsylvania Council on the Arts. Critical work has appeared in *The Denver Quarterly*, *The Pennsylvania Review*, and other journals. She is a regular contributor and reviews editor for *Sentence*.

STACEY WAITE received an MFA in poetry from the University of Pittsburgh in 2003 and has published three collections of poems: *Choke* (winner of the 2004 Frank O'Hara Prize in Poetry), *Love Poem to Androgyny* (winner of the 2006 Main Street Rag Chapbook competition), and *the lake has no saint* (winner of the 2008 Snowbound Prize from Tupelo Press). Poems have been published most recently in *Pinch, The Rattling Wall, Cream City Review*, and *Girls with Glasses*. Waite's first full-length collection, *Butch Geography*, is forthcoming from Tupelo Press. She is assistant professor of English at the University of Nebraska Lincoln.

*

ELISE D'HAENE is the author of *Licking Our Wounds*, winner of the Small Press Book Award 1998 for best LGBTQ novel of the year; and *Married*, recipient of the Hemingway Short Story Award. Other short stories have appeared in *Best American Erotica* and *Hers I* and *II*, published by Faber & Faber. D'Haene co-authored *The Red Shoe Diaries* series of books published by Penguin/Berkley, based on the popular Showtime Network erotic series of the same name. She also wrote several episodes for that series; other screenwriting credits include *The Little Mermaid II* for Disney and the drama series *Wind on Water* for NBC. She holds a BA in English from Oakland University and Masters and PhD degrees in psychology from the University of Southern California.

CELESTE GAINEY is the author of *In the land of speculation & seismography*, a chapbook published by Seven Kitchens Press in their 2011 Summer Kitchen Series and selected by Eloise Klein Healy as a runner-up for the 2010 Robin Becker Chapbook Prize. Gainey has been nominated for a Pushcart Prize and has been a guest on *Prosody*, the public radio show on NPR-affiliate WYEP-FM. Her poems have appeared or are forthcoming in *Columbia Poetry Review, BLOOM, Wild Apples, Madroad: The Breadline Press West Coast*

Anthology, Long Island Sounds, Girls With Glasses, and *Writers At Work*. She has had a long career as a lighting designer for both film and architecture. She holds a BFA in film and television from New York University and an MFA in creative writing/ poetry from Carlow University.

LIANE ELLISON NORMAN is the author of two chapbooks: *Roundtrip*, published by Yesterday's Parties in 2012, and *Driving Near the Old Federal Arsenal*, published in 2011 by Finishing Line Press. Norman has also published two books of poetry, *The Duration of Grief* and *Keep*, a biography, a novel and many articles, essays, and reviews. She has published poems in *The Fourth River, Hot Metal Press, 5AM, North American Review, Kestrel*, and the *Come Together: Imagine Peace* anthology. She won the Wisteria Prize in 2006 from Paper Journey Press.

ABBEY WAMBOLDT is a creative writing major at Carlow University with a concentration in poetry. She is the inaugural winner of the Marilyn P. Donnelly Award in Poetry for undergraduate writers at Carlow University and was published in Carlow's literary magazine, *The Critical Point*. She is the emcee for The Hungry Sphinx Reading Series.

SARAH WILLIAMS-DEVEREUX teaches poetry for the Madwomen in the Attic, and is a transformative language artist. Her work has been published in *Sampsonia Way Magazine, Pittsburgh City Paper, The New Yinzer's Pittsburgh Love Stories* anthology, and the online journal *SubtleTea*. She is the co-author of the research monograph *Our Stories, Our Selves: A3P: The African American Arts Project: A Study of African American Young Adult Arts Participation* (PITT ARTS, University of Pittsburgh, 2006). She is pursuing her CAPF certification in poetry therapy.

Books of Note

BY PATRICIA DOBLER:

— *Collected Poems*, Autumn House Press, 2005.
— *UXB*, Mill Hunk Books, 1991.
— *Talking to Strangers*, University of Wisconsin Press, 1986 Brittingham Prize in Poetry.
— *Forget Your Life*, chapbook, University of Nebraska Press, 1982.

BY ELLIE WYMARD:

— *Talking Steel Towns: The Women and Men of America's Steel Valley*, Carnegie Mellon University Press, 2007.
— *Conversations with Uncommon Women: Insights from Women Who've Risen above Life's Challenges to Achieve Extraordinary Success*, AMACOM, 1999.
— *Men on Divorce: Conversations with Ex-Husbands*, Hay House, 1994.
— *Divorced Women, New Lives*, Ballantine Books, 1990.

BY JANE COLEMAN: *(additional titles not listed)*

— *Tumbleweed*, Dorchester Publishing, 2008.
— *The White Dove, Poetry of the American West*, High Plains Press, 2007.
— *The Italian Quartet*, Five Star, 2001.
— *The Red Drum*, High Plains Press, 1994.

BY JAN BEATTY:

— *The Switching Yard*, forthcoming, University of Pittsburgh Press, 2013.
— *Ravage*, chapbook, Lefty Blondie Press, 2012.
— *Red Sugar*, University of Pittsburgh Press, 2008.
— *Boneshaker*, University of Pittsburgh Press, 2002.
— *Mad River*, University of Pittsburgh Press, 1995.
— *Ravenous*, chapbook, State Street Press, 1995.

BY ELLEN MCGRATH SMITH:

— *A Dog Makes His Rounds and Other Poems*, chapbook, Another Thing Press, 2002.

BY STACEY WAITE:

— *Butch Geography*, forthcoming, 2013.
— *the lake has no saint*, chapbook, Tupelo Press, 2010.
— *Love Poem to Androgyny*, chapbook, Main Street Rag, 2006.
— *Choke*, chapbook, Thorngate Road Press, 2004.

BY ELISE D'HAENE:

— *Licking Our Wounds*, The Permanent Press Publishing Company, 1997.

BY CELESTE GAINEY:

— *In the land of speculation & seismography*, chapbook, Seven Kitchens Press, 2011.

BY LIANE ELLISON NORMAN:

— *Roundtrip*, chapbook, Yesterday's Parties Press, 2012.
— *Driving Near the Old Federal Arsenal*, chapbook,
  Finishing Line Press, 2011.
— *Keep*, Smoke & Mirrors Press, 2008.
— *The Duration of Grief*, Smoke & Mirrors Press, 2005.
— *Stitches in Air: A Novel About Mozart's Mother*,
  Smoke & Mirrors Press, 2001.
— *Hammer of Justice: Molly Rush and the Plowshares Eight*,
  PPI Books, 1990.